Grandmother's Footsteps

Grandmother's Footsteps

PATRICIA LEDWARD

Illustrated by Graham Oakley

MACMILLAN

LONDON · MELBOURNE · TORONTO

1966

MACMILLAN AND COMPANY LIMITED
Little Essex Street London WC2
also Bombay Calcutta Madras Melbourne

THE MACMILLAN COMPANY OF CANADA LIMITED
70 Bond Street Toronto 2

ST MARTIN'S PRESS INC
175 Fifth Avenue New York NY 10010

PRINTED IN GREAT BRITAIN BY
THE BOWERING PRESS PLYMOUTH

For
Peggy and
Charles Richards

THIS BOOK has been written with the knowledge and help of many members of the family it describes. Although all the events in the story are firmly based on truth, some of the incidents may not have happened precisely as I have told them. Nor may people have spoken the exact words I have attributed to them. Therefore, because of this inevitable poetic licence and to spare living people any possible embarrassment I have chosen to give the characters assumed names.

CHAPTER ONE

SUDDENLY everyone was there!

Everyone had arrived at last and was going into the warm, sweet-scented drawing-room. Granny was there already, of course, sitting in her low chair by the Bechstein, beaming like a jolly goddess: and behind her in a straight line, like a grotesque chorus, were the Great-Aunts, those severe, weird Great-Aunts — Tabby the snob; Dooley, who kept her husband in the kitchen because he'd left his job under a cloud; Kennedy, half-hidden in a shawl; the scandalous Sophia, whose misdeeds were only mentioned in whispers.

This glowing afternoon was the summit towards which the year had been climbing day by day, week by week — Christmas at Granny's.

After lunch the uncles had pulled themselves together in their respective homes and joined their wives and children. The exhausted wives were drooping like thirsty plants; the children, up since before dawn, were still bright with excitement and restless as eels.

In Putney, half a mile up the hill from Granny's house, Bernard, the sculptor, adjusted his pince-nez and squared his shoulders ready for the ordeal of going-out-with-the-family. A shy, susceptible, gifted man who worked at his art with relentless fervour, he was only able to love his children from a great distance. He cast a last fond look at his bosomy ladies with their sweetly dimpled stone bottoms and reluctantly closed the studio door behind him.

'All ready then?' he enquired, making a great effort to be pleasant. 'Is this the case with the presents? Do you want me to carry it?'

'You can't expect *me* to,' retorted Dorothy. She was a proud, intelligent, emotional woman, as tricky as a crossword puzzle. Her body was taut as string, her face beautiful; all Bernard's statues had her lovely, Botticelli face. 'Presents,' she hissed, beyond herself with tiredness. 'Always for the family! So narrow! When there's such *real* poverty, such *real* need in the world.'

The world's miseries cut her to the bone; she often felt as though she were carrying the burdens of the dispossessed and unfortunate on her own thin shoulders and she raged inwardly because of their pain and because she had not yet been able to find a solution to the paradoxes of poverty in the midst of plenty.

Bernard frowned.

'I'll carry the case!' cried their middle child, nine-year-old Vicky, sensing the cutting edge of one of those quarrels she so dreaded. Anything to prevent those familiar voices suddenly turning cold and strange and hurting everyone with their strife. Anything to get out of the house, to get started on the Christmas journey through the quiet roads. Always pretending to be something she wasn't, she was now going through a phase of passionately wanting to be a boy: she insisted on having her hair cropped short, wore knee-length boy's socks and often looked rather odd. The greatest compliment she had ever received was hearing two people remark about her: 'Is that a boy or a girl?' Boys had strong biceps and protected their mothers. 'I'll carry it!' She heaved up the case. It fell open.

'You are *silly*,' complained her elder sister Diana. 'Always showing-off!' Diana was charmingly pretty and feminine; she was dying to get to Granny's and display her new dress, a silky, soft affair, apple-green and shimmery. She also had a gorgeously naughty story she was longing to tell Betty and Sarah, the cousins of her own age. She wanted to hear Betty's gusty, cheerful laughter — 'Ho-ho-ho — really? — *what* — oh, ha-ha-ha —'

Ralph, aged five, began to roar and to scratch at the front door. He, too, was pretending. He was a tiger.

Bernard made a final announcement: his voice was firm as a block of marble. 'When we get outside *I* shall go on in front with the case. The rest of you must walk behind. Several yards behind. I shall pretend I don't know you.'

In her bedroom in Chelsea Maud, who was darkly and bewitchingly beautiful and who could never see enough of herself, stood preening in front of the mirror. She adjusted the pearls that had been a present from her husband, Reggie, and she smiled at herself.

'Do I look all wight?' She was never tired of compliments. The family beauty, she liked this fact to be acknowledged frequently. Her little difficulty in pronouncing a strong 'r' was rather attractive; people liked the way she spoke.

'You look perfect, darling.'

Reggie was a painter, a handsome, charming, popular man who had the knack of flattering portraits out of the rich and of landing coveted jobs without arousing any animosity. He possessed rare gifts of encouragement and appreciation and was held in great esteem by all who knew him. His was a life without enemies.

'And the pearls? Are they all wight with the dwess?'

He kissed her long, pale, Pre-Raphaelite neck and reassured her extravagantly, the touch of native Yorkshire in his voice making him sound more sincere than perhaps he really was. Actually the necklace had cost him more than he could afford: but he had long ago convinced himself that Maud was worth any debts he might risk at the bank.

'What about *me*?' Their only child, Sarah, edged herself into this *tête-à-tête*. She was fourteen, with huge, dark, mischievous eyes and dark-brown curls. Everything amused her, everything was funny. When she laughed, which was often, people immediately felt allured, deliciously disturbed. Her mother worried constantly lest some dweadful man might abduct her, seduce her. 'Isn't my dress lovely? I'm sure it'll be the prettiest. Betty and Deborah always wear such arty things. And Diana isn't quite —'

'We are *all* artists in this family,' emphasized Maud, missing the point.

'Anyway, I'm looking forward to my tea!' Sarah patted her tummy. 'I'm looking forward to the presents. To all the people. To everyone admiring my dress and saying how nice I look.'

Joyce, kind, impetuous, sensitive Joyce, who was large and who moved with the fastidious, unexpected grace of a heifer, was finding Christmas more than she had bargained for this year. A new baby in the house and not quite enough money to manage comfortably on was putting too many loyalties to the test.

4

Baby Jocelyn was cross. A great fist of wind was pummelling his stomach; he found the pain intolerable. The little sitting-room in Barnes rang with his shrieks.

'*Angus* — the dill-water — don't just sit there —' Joyce's face was chalky with anxiety. 'He might *die* —'

Jocelyn drew his knees up to his chin, lashed out with his fists. Agony added weight to his punch; Joyce winced as he struck her on the nose.

'Ha-ha — going to be a boxer this one — ha-ha — ' Angus, the bluff, the hearty, gave his son a congratulatory slap on the back. He had just woken up from his usual afternoon nap (a habit that his wife found exceedingly tiresome at times) and he felt gay as a puppy. His treatment broke up the clot of wind; it rushed around the tortured little body, leaping out here and there in small explosions. They all felt relieved.

'Where's Bruce?' Joyce worried over the next problem. 'Angus, for heaven's sake find him. We're going to be late for the party. Find him, Angus. He's sure to be doing something he shouldn't.'

Three-year-old Bruce was. He had grabbed a sponge from the bathroom and was washing the walls.

'If *you* hadn't been asleep — on Christmas Day — with all that washing-up — ' Joyce rounded on Angus with the pent-up truth.

He beamed back at her amiably, thinking that she looked uncommonly fine in her fury. He knew he was lazy. He knew he should struggle against his afternoon sleepiness. But on this lovely Day he was impervious to feelings of guilt or inadequacy. Flakes of snow drifted past the window. Soon the trees would be lighting up in the little windows of the houses. It was thrilling! It was joy!

'Keep your hair on, old dear,' he riposted lovingly.

Clara put the finishing touches to her daughters' toilet. A plump, busy, self-disciplined woman who did most things very well, she was shrewd and sympathetic. Her widowed mother's eldest daughter, she had spent much of her youth listening to adult anxieties: this had made her careful. Her tidy, tasteful house near Battersea Bridge was visibly the home of someone who knew that every penny mattered.

'Betty, if you touch your hair ribbon once more you won't come,' she admonished her elder daughter. 'This is the fifth time I've had to do it.'

'Ha-ha-ha — ' responded Betty gaily, secure in the knowledge that her mother's threatened punishments were never carried out.

Clara's deft fingers arranged the broad black ribbon once more. 'There — that's perfect! Don't you dare!'

She gave a little nod of satisfaction at the beautiful winged bow, hovering just above Betty's smooth hair like a blackbird, and turned to Deborah.

'Now you.'

But Deborah was a timid child. She had not dared to touch those shining ringlets twined so laboriously round her mother's finger.

Betty, suddenly irritated by her sister's Lord Fauntleroy appearance, gave her a dig with her elbow. Deborah started to cry.

'What's the matter? What's the matter?'

'Betty pinched me.'

'I didn't! You liar! I only nudged!'

'You're a naughty — '

'Sorry I've kept you waiting, me dears!' Salisbury, who always kept everybody waiting, came down from the bathroom wiping shaving-lather off his face. Although he often looked forlorn, even lost, he was actually an alert, joky man. A sculptor by training he

6

was a man who could make anything. In some ways his facility was his undoing: his easy skill robbed him, led him astray into unprofitable byways. Any deprived child could touch him for a toy; his sure hands would quickly heal an uneasy piece of furniture. The fatherless boy next door could, with a look, charm trains from him, perfect models of historic trains made with infinite care and given for love; whereas the man who was paying for a fountain-figure, or a bust of his wife, had to fret and fume and perhaps pass the work on to somebody else. Clara had long ago given up the attempt to change her unorthodox, soft-hearted husband.

'I've made a wonderful present for old Johnnie,' he chuckled. 'When he sees it! His face!'

'Will Molly approve?'

'You wait! Now, come along, me dears. The chariot's outside.'

He adored his family; nothing was too much trouble for him where they were concerned. Scooping up his daughters he went out into the road where their old car waited, muffled up in snow.

'In you get. Comfy? All settled? Off we go then.'

'Christmas is coming and very glad am I,
I shall go to Granny's and have a piece of pie — '

sang Clara softly as the car clanked along the white roads.

'— and have a piece of pie,
I don't mean the magpie which sits upon the house
I mean a bit of mincepie which is so very nice.'

The snow fell thickly. Small, illuminated trees shone out from innumerable windows. The faithful lamplighter with his long pole patrolled the roads, kindling sparks in the growing darkness.

7

And then, suddenly, everyone was there!

They clustered in the porch of the house Granny shared with her eldest son, John, and Mollie, his wife. The door was flung open and they were inside: the house smelt of cinnamon, sage, thyme, pomanders, cloves, sweet-scented leaves of *Pelargonium capitatum*, apples, resin.

Snow melted off the children's clothes, dripped down from their eyelashes. One or two of them looked guiltily down at the little puddles.

'Doesn't matter! Doesn't matter!' sang out Mollie, rosy and buxom in her blue silk dress. 'It used to snow much more than this when your Uncle Johnnie and I lived in Russia. And when we were escaping from the Revolution and the wolves and the Bolshies —'

Those who could squeezed past her; they had heard this story many times before.

But Dorothy took a stand, as usual, and listened and allowed her children to listen.

'It's really Mollie who does all the work for these Christmas parties,' Dorothy would tell her children. 'She has a dreadful time in this house. I don't know how she puts up with it. Your Granny grumbling. Your Uncle Johnnie shouting. Mollie's a marvel.'

The others didn't think so. They thought she was the very opposite of a marvel and were astonished that Dorothy, with her sharp intelligence, refused to recognize what a dreadful woman she really was. Not at all Dorothy's type, Dorothy the spartan, Dorothy the passionate puritan. What Mollie had done, and continued to do, was far, far worse than Great-Aunt Sophia's original sin.

But Dorothy and Mollie were allies, were daughters-in-law. Both had obstinate, brilliantly clever husbands; both had the same jealous mother-in-law. And, in any case, Dorothy often used her wits to avoid seeing the things she preferred to ignore; she was an adept at turning a blind eye when she chose.

Johnnie was an inspired engineer, a financial wizard, charming when he chose to be, entirely selfish, very fat. Granny adored him. For Mollie, whose origins were obscure and Irish, she had an abiding dislike and distaste.

Mollie was broad and apple-cheeked, like a wooden Russian doll; she had small, twinkling eyes and a wild temper. The children loved her — until the superior, and prejudiced, knowledge of the grown-ups corrupted them; even then they continued to remember her with warmth and amusement — and with fascination because she served an anarchic way of life that was forbidden them, because her gods were Dionysian and her rites bacchic. She was so jolly, so funny, able to tell such thrilling stories of the parts of her life she wanted known. Oh, those wolves howling in the Siberian darkness! Those Red people rushing over the ice with their glinting sabres! That ballet dancer who made everyone weep when she danced the Dying Swan! Oh! Oh!

Some rooms shrink when crowded, needing emptiness to emphasize their space. But the drawing-room into which everyone now pressed seemed, by some magic of correct proportion and decoration, to grow larger.

Granny sat on her low chair by the Bechstein, flanked by her sisters, severe in their weird black dresses. She was knitting, talking, kissing, complimenting. This easy ability to do several things simultaneously had been her salvation. Her hair was still nut-brown, even though she was in her late sixties, her complexion clear as a pretty girl's.

The children pushed forward to kiss Granny; after

which they were grabbed, one by one, by a little man whose hair stood up like a teddy bear's.

'Yum, yum, yum — I've got you!' He kissed them with exuberant greed. 'Yum, yum, yum — can't get away, can you!'

The delighted, embarrassed children squirmed and giggled, wiped away his tickly moustaches, cried *stop, stop*. This was their courtesy Uncle, Uncle Merrie, another artist, Head of Goldsmiths' College of Art. He had no children of his own but was an old friend of the family and allowed to play the part of Father Christmas every year.

'Such a surprise after tea. Yum, yum, yum. Such a joke.'

Deborah edged away, frightened by his affection. 'I know,' she said haughtily, 'you'll dress up as Father Christmas.' He was so little that she could almost look down her nose at him. After years of baffled understanding she had at last solved the mystery. She felt immensely adult. 'You always do.'

'Just you wait and see! Such a surprise! Such a joke!'

He bobbed up and down, infecting the younger children with his excitement. Pandemonium threatened.

'I want my tea,' roared Johnnie, shaking his cheeks. '*Tea! Mollie!*'

He had an obsessive passion for food. In his boyhood he had often been hungry and had had to suffer mutely, pretending it was nothing and that it didn't really matter.

'Mollie — remember the *shrimps*!'

Mollie appeared round the door; her face was very red.

'Shouldn't be surprised if she hadn't been at it again,' whispered Clara. 'On her own. In the kitchen.'

Dorothy threw a shocked, piercing glance at Clara.

It was not the remark that disturbed her, but the fact that Clara was sitting on Salisbury's lap. What a way to behave! Such an unseemly public exhibition of private affection! So vulgar.

Bernard brooded by himself in a corner. Family gatherings made him melancholy, bringing out all the latent pessimism in his nature. Limitations caged him in. He was not a snob, not a social climber — but at times like this he longed passionately to belong to a different class, to associate with people whose lives had never been conditioned by need, who were ceremonious, courteous, witty. The family was a gaol. He thought with yearning of the cool, green, bronze girl in his studio, his lovely 'Awakening'. He had never offered her for sale, knowing that he could not bear to part with this image of beauty and truth. A sculptor could arrest the fleeing moments of joy and make them eternal: alone among artists it was the sculptor who could record the passage of time with most permanence. Paintings faded, music died away to an echo, and where were the great libraries of Alexandria, where the poems of the Sumerians? He took a sketch book from his pocket and began to make quick drawings.

'Shrimps, did you say? I'm just peeling the little beggars for your Lordship.' The Irish in Mollie rolled out juicily in her voice.

Granny cleared her throat loudly and said, 'Where's Sarah? I haven't kissed her yet.'

'Isn't my dress pretty?' Instantly responsive to this cue that promised her everyone's attention, Sarah swayed provocatively across the room, holding out her skirts. 'I chose the material. Mummy made the dress. To my design.'

'Swank!' remarked Betty kindly. She believed in always saying what she thought and she either didn't mind very much about hurting people's feelings now and then, or else she didn't see that she did. After all, she reasoned, whatever one said it was only an opinion.

'What about me?' purred Maud, smiling at her reflection in the copper coal scuttle. 'Is my dwess smart?'

'Bit too,' retorted Betty unerringly.

'I've got something to tell you.' Diana saw in a flash that her own dress could not compete with Sarah's red and white flounces and she staked her reputation for sophistication on her scandalous story. 'Come here!' She beckoned to Betty and Sarah.

'Is it R?' asked Sarah, meaning *rude*.

'*Awfully.*'

They huddled together. Vicky and Deborah, four or five years younger, hung on the fringe of this sophisticated conclave and looked coldly at each other. Deborah thought Vicky looked peculiar. Vicky thought Deborah looked a cissy. Bet she couldn't climb that tree on the Common! Bet I could get her down in a fight!

Deborah started to whimper.

'What is it?' Clara came to the rescue of her youngest. 'What's the matter?'

'They won't tell me. They won't let me hear the story.'

Vicky listened, ears pricked for the something *awful*.

'Yes, well you see, it was dark. And the lavatory was outside, you see. Well, she went in and she lifted up —'

Ralph, still acting the part of a tiger, sprang into their midst with a roar.

'*What* did you say she did?' asked Betty.

'Tea's ready.' Mollie bobbed round the door again. 'And the blessed shrimps are in their birthday suits.'

'TEA!' roared Johnnie, and he played some loud, Wagnerian chords on the piano.

Maud, as usual, made straight for the most comfortable chair. Clara, in her self-effacing way, chose the most awkward one. The rest scrambled for any place they could find.

Unlike the drawing-room the kitchen could not possibly be enlarged by any miracle or magic. It groaned and creaked with the effort of accommodating this hungry multitude.

It was a feast fit for a pagan. In her hard, Victorian youth, when she had lived in the dense, drunken Potteries, Granny had belonged to the Band of Hope and had become acquainted with a strict, lecturing, Nonconformist God Whom she had not liked very much and from Whom she had been relieved to escape. In her very old age she found God again, the mild God of the Christian Scientists, and she was amazed to discover that He was a God of love. But in the years between she was too busy to call on Him and her rare festivals were unsanctified.

Oh, those Christmas teas! Those crisp tarts and pies oozing with mincemeat, the shortbread stuck with sugar and almonds, the wobbling, smacking jellies drowning in cream, the sumptuous fruit salads. Oh, the sausage rolls, the ham sandwiches, the ginger beer, the dark, rich fruit cakes, made by Mollie, who always poured into them a bottle of what she fancied, the soggy cakes whisked together by Granny in the twinkling of an eye and riotously iced in an untidy dash of inspiration. Oh, those plates of delicious Staffordshire oatcakes. The crackers, the paper chains, the floating balloons.

In the lean days of the next war the children would dream of those Christmas teas. When they grew up they would try to make their own parties conform to the same rich pattern. They would heap up their fires with the same ardour, would do their best to create temporary oases of loving kindness and fun even though the world stormed outside the windows.

'If seven men with seven wives had seven bites every seven minutes —' John gloated over the dish of shrimps from Harrods, ordered for him alone — 'how long would it take them to finish all this?' Food in abundance relaxed him, made him almost gentle.

Crackers started banging. Out fell rings, indoor fireworks, whistles. People put on crinkly paper hats and were instantly transformed into characters from comic operas. Salisbury laughed till the tears came.

'What keeps running but never leaves its bed?' read out Sarah.

'Something R,' suggested Betty.

'There was a young lady called Grace,' started Angus, 'Who had a remarkable face —'

'Arnold Bennett wrote a much better limerick in my autograph album,' boasted Clara.

They were all rather proud of the successful Arnold Bennett. He had put members of the family into some of his novels. He had taken Bernard sailing with him among the islands of the Baltic.

'Listen,' said Clara. 'It went like this —

> There was a young man of Montrose
> Who had pockets in none of his clothes,
> When asked by his lass
> Where he carried his brass,
> Answered 'Darling, I pay through the nose.'

'Arnold's made plenty of brass,' commented John.

'When I wrote and asked him for a donation to the Artists' Benevolent Fund,' remarked Bernard, 'he replied "*My dear Bernard, do you take me for a fool. How would you respond if I asked you for a donation to the Writers' Benevolent Fund?*"'

There was a small silence. For a number of years Granny's small income had been eked out by a grant from the Artists' Fund.

'Arnold Bennett treats his wife abominably,' announced Dorothy, defending the rights of wives as well as widows and all other underdogs.

'You've always got an axe to grind, Dorothy,' shouted John. 'You're so damn censorious.'

Mollie pushed the cake at him. 'This one's got a whole bottle of Guinness in it.' She winked at Dorothy. 'You mustn't mind his Lordship, darlin'.'

Dorothy didn't mind. She loved a good argument. Warmed by the food and the people, she felt easy now and was almost allowing herself the indulgence of enjoying the party. The poor and the starving still roamed the dark world — there, outside in the snow — but so agreeable was the present that she could almost forget about them.

The time was at the very end of the '20's, approaching the finale of the post-war boom. It was a time when the rich could still get richer with tolerable honesty and the poor could sink right down to the degrading depths without anyone making much fuss. A Labour Government was on the verge of being elected in England. In Germany the torchlight rallies of Hitler were becoming more frequent. In America Wall Street was about to crash.

Under the comfortable surface uncomfortable ideas were beginning to stir. Gentle people who would go out of their way to rescue a fly drowning in a milk jug discussed violent ways to establish an impossible equality. The young were openly rejecting God. The elder generation, many of them wounded to the quick of their spirit by the Great War, were trying to bring up their children according to the rules of that golden, extraordinary pre-1914 era, when order was immutable, happiness without end, conventions decently observed. The younger generation, torn, uncertain, feeling in its growing bones that another war was imminent, did its best to be loyal to two worlds and often broke apart under the strain. Schizophrenia was quite a common malady.

But no one could have guessed, looking at the laughing people round this table, that there were undercurrents of terror once more pulling at the roots of society. True, John did rave now and then about everything being the fault of those damn Bolshies: but he had been British Consul in Moscow for a while and knew what he was talking about. And Dorothy might make impassioned speeches about the slums and the hungry miners and make everyone feel guilty: but she was inclined to be unbalanced and it wasn't necessary to take her uncomfortable idealism seriously.

Granny beamed over the top of five huge teapots and surveyed the gathering with joy and satisfaction. She felt so proud of her children: they had turned out so well, were so successful.

John was climbing to the very top of the great world of international engineering. One day he would be rich and powerful. How sad it was that he was childless. All the fault of that *impossible* Mollie. If he ever decided to leave Mollie she would help him all she could.

Bernard, too, was climbing up to the top. He had inherited all his father's gifts and was said by many to be the most talented sculptor of his generation. He won endless prizes and competitions. And Dorothy, who came from a good family and had once been rich, was quite a feather in their cap; she was devoted to Bernard (it had been a match of great love) and had, therefore, to be forgiven many things.

Maud had passed all her exams at the Slade School of Art with ease, had grown more beautiful year by year, had married well. It was rumoured that Reggie was almost certain to be the next Principal of the Royal College of Art.

Clara, who had fulfilled her cherished ambition that one, at least, of the children should be a musician.

Joyce, her darling, her baby, her comfort.

They were her children. *Hers. She* had created their successes. *She* had urged them on to triumph, encouraged them, loved them — all by herself.

She reached out for her fourth mince tart and ate it very quickly.

'Better belly bust than good food be lost!' cackled Great-Aunt Sophia by her side. 'Do you remember how we ate, all those years ago, when dear Mr. Bolt and I —'

'For goodness' sake, Sophia, don't rake up your dreadful past,' rapped out Granny. 'You've drunk too much ginger beer.'

'What was your dreadful past?' asked Sarah hopefully. 'Were you a loose woman?' She wasn't sure what this meant but it sounded very funny.

'Saa — waa —'

'Has anyone seen sausages hanging up?' asked Salisbury, stepping quickly in to defend the family honour.

'Yes —' everyone shouted. This was one of the first sights in the world.

'No you haven't. They hang *down.*'

Granny sighed with relief and took up her knitting. She could always rely on Salisbury. Sophia tried to hide behind the tea cosy. Granny counted stitches and blessings.

The grandchildren were shaping well, too. Sarah

would go far with her looks and vivacity. Deborah had just won a scholarship to the High School: Betty had a scholarship as well. The babies, Bruce and Jocelyn, she adored too much to be able to think about reasonably. Bernard's children? What was it Dorothy *didn't* do? Ralph, so fair and fine-boned, looked fragile and Vicky was too excitable. And sometimes Diana worried her terribly — the sweet child took everything so seriously, would burst into tears or lose her temper at the smallest thing. They were all darlings, of course, but what *was* it?

'What did you say happened?' Sarah whispered to Diana. 'That *awful* story?'

'Well, you see, her fiancé was there already,' continued Diana happily. 'And she sat down on his lap! Wasn't it terrible! Of course she couldn't look him in the face after that. She broke off the engagement at once.'

She gazed at her cousins, waiting for their shocked appreciation.

'How disgusting!' pronounced the lovely Sarah.

'I don't believe it!' Betty had a mathematician's mind and liked her facts to be correct.

'Uncle Merrie, dear, hadn't you better see if Father Christmas is coming down the road?' suggested Granny. 'He may have been knocking and we haven't heard. Hadn't you better?'

'Yes, yes, yes. I'll run along and see.' He clasped his hands together in ecstasy. He loved acting his part. And this year he had his little joke to play. 'I'll go at once.'

'And I've got to fix the tree,' remembered John, suddenly serious and quiet.

'I'll come and give you a hand, old chap.' Reggie pushed back his chair.

The daughters cleared the table. The children heaped up their treasures from the crackers. Ralph slipped out into the white garden and stood listening to hear if he could catch the distant roar of the suburban trains. Or was it tigers he hoped to surprise, hunting through the forests of the night?

In twos and threes they all drifted back to the drawing-room.

The lights were out and the flickering fire suggested cavernous, unexplored depths. It smoothed the hushed faces of the children and bestowed serenity on the grown-ups. They were all moved by that feeling of holy peace and mystery that is the essence of Christmas.

'*Stille nacht, heilige nacht —*' Johnnie's melodious baritone sang out from the depths of the tree.

And that peace that passes all understanding possessed them all. No one spoke, or moved. Granny put aside her knitting and took her two youngest grandchildren on her lap. She softly sang the tune to Johnnie's words.

'*Alles schläft, einsam wacht* — Now Reggie, you can switch on.'

With a soft click the tree sprang out of the shadows.

Surprised by joy the children gasped and clutched each other. This year, for the first time, the sombre branches were garlanded with coloured lights. They glowed like jewels, beckoned like distant windows in a benighted forest, shone up from the black pool of the Bechstein.

The door creaked. This would be Father Christmas shaking snow from his beard.

But it was only Salisbury, regretting to say that Father Christmas had been unavoidably detained. 'So as not to disappoint you, though, the Lady Mayoress of

Fulham has graciously consented to honour us with her presence and distribute the presents. The Lady Mayoress —'

A tiny figure tottered round the door on unfamiliar high heels.

'It's Uncle Merrie again,' said Deborah sourly.

Two or three cushions gave him an immense, top-heavy bosom. He wore the fur coat snatched by Mollie from the hands of the pursuing Bolshies and a wonderful hat he had concocted the night before, a frivolous confection of ribbons, flowers, feathers.

'How gorgeous!' laughed Sarah. 'Oh dear, how *funny*!'

Her alluring laughter acted on Uncle Merrie like a spell. He held out his arms, blew kisses, laid his hands expressively on his cushions, bowed and curtsied in all directions.

'Charmed to be here! Utterly!' His voice was a squeak.

Sarah laughed so much she had a pain.

'I shall want one or two helpers. To distribute the largesse.' One of his cushions slipped down to the floor. 'Blast!' he said, and kicked it out of the way.

The distribution began. Clara played carols on the piano as it proceeded. The children reverently touched the coloured wrapping paper, fingered the tinsel ribbon, imagined what might be inside. No one was allowed to unwrap anything until the heap under the branches was entirely demolished.

At last the tree was denuded of its gifts. The Lady Mayoress curtsied herself out of the room, losing her other breast on the way, and reappeared as darling Uncle Merrie. The air whispered and crackled with tissue paper, murmured with the oohs and aahs of satisfaction. An atmosphere of unimaginable glamour filled the room. The most ordinary things were exciting; even a notebook and pencil from Woolworths was exactly what one had been longing for. And Granny's untidy parcels of her own home-made fudge were exotic sweetmeats fit for a Sheikh of Araby.

Ralph sat down on the floor and mopped up his fudge at one go. The other children wandered among the parents saying thank-you, while they in their turn feigned delight at childish gifts. Bernard, seeing the end of the party at last in view, looked happy for the first time. Dorothy suddenly remembered that her house was small and ill-planned, with no cupboards to speak of, and she said with a groan, 'All these presents! I don't know *where* we're going to put them all.' Johnnie bellowed with laughter at Salisbury's mysterious present, said he'd been wanting something like that for a long time and refused to show it to Mollie. Mollie looked aggrieved.

'Now for some games! Now for our party pieces!' Granny felt the interest beginning to sag. 'Pencils! Paper! Consequences!' When it came to parties and amusements she was tireless.

People allowed themselves to be organized into heads, bodies and tails, telegrams, consequences. Miraculous creations — monsters and unearthly beings and amalgams of every person in the room — emerged from the folded papers of the first game.

'Where's Mollie?' asked Dorothy in the middle of a drawing.

'Gone into the kitchen,' laughed Maud. 'Where else! For a spot of quiet comfort.'

'I'll comfort her if she needs it,' said Dorothy and wondered why they all laughed. 'What's the joke? She's gone to finish the washing-up.'

'She's gone because she doesn't know how to write,'

explained Clara. 'You know that. And to have a little —'

'Stop it! Leave her alone!' shouted Johnnie.

'I'm going to find her,' said Dorothy.

'Let's play charades,' cried Granny. 'Or dumb crambo. You first, children. Go outside and make up your minds.'

They went into the kitchen to decide. There they found Dorothy and Mollie in each other's arms. Mollie was saying, 'I can't bear it much longer, Dorothy darlin',' and Dorothy was murmuring. 'I know, I know.' Feeling slightly shocked, the children went into the bedroom for their discussion.

'What shall we have?'

'Let's have Aunt.' Sarah took the lead. 'We can dress up in their hats and coats. And peck each other scornfully on the cheek.'

'A for *atishoo*,' suggested Diana. 'We can sneeze.'

'And all fall down,' added Vicky.

'N — *naughty*,' mused Deborah. 'We can smack each other.'

'T —' pondered Betty. '*Thumb*. We'll hold them in the air. And suck them.'

'What about U?'

They all wondered.

'*Umbilical!*' announced Sarah with a laugh. 'We'll all march round the room pointing to our tummies.'

They did. Nobody guessed the word.

'More,' pleaded Granny. 'More.'

Betty and Deborah recited poems by A. A. Milne, Diana sang, Sarah did the Charleston; Mollie came back from the kitchen cheered by Dorothy's sympathy and repeated that she had seen Pavlova dance 'The Dying Swan' in St. Petersburg and had wept for joy. Uncle Merrie stood on his head. Salisbury conjured. Vicky

22

declaimed a mysterious poem by Walter de la Mare, Ralph was sick with excitement and too much fudge, Dorothy said too much of this sort of thing was bad for children and it was time to go.

Strong movements of departure agitated the room. Granny held out imploring arms.

'You needn't go yet. Stay a little longer.' She bent double over the coal scuttle, broad as a washerwoman, and shovelled on fuel. Flames roared up the chimney.

'You'll have us on fire, Mother,' cautioned John.

'Don't go — don't go —' A moment's fear clutched her heart. With her dear ones around her she was safe from the spectre of loneliness that sometimes haunted her, from that fear of homelessness and poverty that had been her quiet, faithful companion most of her life. 'Stay a little longer.'

She needed them all about her. They were her protection, her reason for being brave. Without them she felt withered and appallingly vulnerable.

'Let's have a sinG sonG.' When she was anxious her Staffordshire accent was very noticeable. 'A sinG sonG!' The final G's were clear. 'I love to hear you all sin — GinG. Like when you were all little.'

She had a secret fear that nagged her when she was tired and alone, a fear that Mollie might one day persuade Johnnie to turn her out of the house. And then where would she go? The dear, familiar room faded in front of her eyes. In its place she saw an endless street, beneath a cold, dirty sky. As she walked on and on and on all the doors shut against her, one after the other. She was alone. In a squalid alley a man fell on his face and a thin, pale child wept. Granny shuddered. Oh no, not *that*.

'Sin — G!' she commanded.

Joyce, noticing her mother's sudden pallor, put her arms round her and gave her a kiss. 'You're coming to see *us* tomorrow, Mother darling.'

'Sin — G! All of you together!'

Beating time with her knitting-needle Granny started off in a sweet, quavering voice:

> 'Ten o'clock the rain begins to fall
> And Nelly still from home,
> Tenderly her loving name we call
> Oh whither does she roam —

Come on! Everyone together. Join in.'

This song had nothing to do with Christmas, but it expressed her mood and exorcized her fear. Music had such a power of consolation. Music never failed.

> 'Bless the child! I fear her little feet
> Have carried her astray —'

'Good-bye, Mother,' said Bernard resolutely. 'You're coming to see *us* on New Year's Day.'

> 'Wake the boys to look for Nelly,
> Stay not for the dawn —'

went on Granny, defying them to leave her.

But she could not halt the inevitable exodus. In their threes and fours the family went out into the snow, taking with them a portion of the kind, loving atmosphere of the house. Even Bernard, hurrying back to his stone loves, had mellowed: he actually allowed his family to walk with him; he actually carried the sleepy Ralph on his back.

'What *did* happen to Nelly?' wondered Betty as their car took them homewards.

'I expect they found her,' Salisbury reassured her. 'I'm sure she was all right.'

'What did Aunt Sophia do?' asked Sarah, walking arm in arm with both her parents.

'You were tewwible, darling. I was so ashamed.'

'Was it really *bad*? Did she kill someone?'

'She mawwied her stepfather.'

'Was that all?'

'In those days it was a dweadful thing to do. They had to wun away to Scotland to get mawwied.'

'I always thought —' Sarah had hoped for bigamy at the very least.

'It meant that she was not only Gwanny's sister, but her step-mother as well. It was dweadfully embawwassing for them all.'

John and Mollie drew up their arm-chairs on either side of the bright fire. Granny pushed her chair back a little, took up her knitting and went on making body belts for the babies.

'You might have showed me Salisbury's present,' grumbled Mollie.

'Tomorrow, old girl, tomorrow.'

The softly shaded lamp sketched caricatures of them all on the wall: John's cheeks were like balloons, Mollie's bosom was a shelf on which her chin rested like a ginger jar and Granny's nose had the pride of a ship's figurehead.

CHAPTER TWO

GRANNY's haughty nose was a reminder of those distant centuries (before James II in his terror finally relegated the fortunes of the Stuarts to outer darkness) when kings had divine rights and courtiers owned lands and fat moneybags.

Every family has one member whose self-appointed mission it is to keep the home flags flying, who will not rest until some obscure nobleman has been dug out of the parish registers. Cousin Cedric, a small, rosy engraver who in his later years found he could make as good a living out of genealogy as out of art, had with loving precision traced the family right back to the thirteenth century. He carried a copy of his findings in the inside pocket of his jacket and out it sprang at the first whisper of polite interest.

'You see here — right back to Le Sieur de Bois Dauphin —' his voice assumed an arrogance that was not natural to it. '— yes, via the Groves of Brownhill, the Groves of Porthill, the Groves of Cheddleton and Burslem, the Groves of Henly Hall —'

There were Groves throughout Staffordshire, firmly rooted in the coal and clay that lay under those undulating green meadows and chaotic towns. Dear Cousin Cedric was too fair-minded to ignore the more common-or-garden Groves altogether, but he himself would have been the first to admit, with a wicked twinkle, that it was really more interesting, and more profitable to concentrate on the gifted and the lucky, those whose destiny had lifted them up into the bright light of wealth, success, leadership.

'— yes, all in Burke's, mark you, all with coats of arms — look — a fine lion, isn't he? Ramping so proudly.'

Sprigs of oak fructed, bundles of wood lay fesswise, groves budded, lions ramped — and to the twentieth-century descendants it all had about as much significance as a mammoth's tusk left over from the ice age. Such excessively specialized knowledge tended to batter the listener into a stupor. Did it really matter — those streams of family blood issuing from the past — those gnarled Groves of antiquity —

To Cousin Cedric it mattered and he would have said with good reason that his dedication was unselfish and invaluable.

'Nuisance about the Battle of the Boyne, you know —' (the intervening centuries melted away at the sound of his burning pride). 'Colonel Richard Groves had all his lands confiscated, you know, and the family had to take to potting after that. Rather a come down. Though, mind you, some of them developed great talents and made a lot of money out of their bit of Staffordshire clay —

And some of them made fine pottery figures and their names became famous and people bid high for their work in the great auction rooms. And their artistic skill stretched away into the future and lay waiting quietly for unborn generations to recognize

27

their inheritance, to realize the potential wealth and joy to be found in their own restless, shapely hands.

The only legacy visibly allotted to Granny from the aristocratic heyday of the flourishing Groves (those Groves who had loyally served in the Royal households of Tudors and Stuarts) was her abundant strength and energy, a complete absence of pettiness that had a natural nobility about it — and that proud nose.

Few places could have been uglier than the Potteries when she was born in the middle of Victoria's reign. Squalid homes crowded higgledy-piggledy up and down the hills that had once been so green and pleasant; the geometrical shapes of kilns and chimneys dominated the open sky. Dark, deep canals, whispering of foul deeds and tragic accidents, wound secretly through the backways; a pall of smoke endlessly pressed down on the low roofs. Everywhere was grime, drunkenness, poverty, disease.

But Annie, crammed like a warm, hungry fledgling into the humble little house in Waterloo Road, Burslem, with her parents and her seven brothers and sisters, was probably unaware of the appalling conditions that social historians were later to describe in such grisly terms. In her merry, loving childhood she was protected from evil by plates piled high with food, by layers of flannel petticoats and hats bedecked with feathers and ribbons, by fires that leapt and crackled in the grate, by the cosy bodies of her sisters whose bed she shared — two or three to a bed, snug and close.

In summer the towing-paths along the dark canals were an escape route to the open fields. In winter the frost transformed the greasy water into glittering highways along which the skaters soared and dipped like birds. In summer every scrap of earth in the small back yard nourished a fragrant, contented plant. Honey-suckle, sweet-briar, lavender, tobacco plants, stock — on those stuffy Victorian summer nights the scent rose up into the small back bedrooms, intoxicating the children, who tossed and turned in their hot beds. In winter when the wind screamed down the interminable road, drowning even the whine and clank of the trams, the good local coal would feed the ravenous flames until they shone with the brilliance of autumn trees. Round the chenille-covered table, under the lamplight, the family would snuggle, knitting, sewing, drawing, reading aloud — all busy as beavers. The one real vice was idleness.

Sometimes when the autumn gales banged about in the sky and the moon danced crazily in and out of tattered clouds the cosy family might talk of witches and call out eerie memories from the fastness of the mind. Staffordshire was notorious for its witches. Later, lying safe in bed, the children would go on whispering legends to each other.

'And they say she can talk to the dead —'

'Have you heard about the witches' feasts? They steal babies and they eat 'em. Annie, stop it! You're pushing me out of bed!'

'They don't! Not babies! Not *really*!' In her delicious terror Annie wrapped herself more tightly round her sister.

'That's what I heard tell. And in Burslem churchyard, right here, have you heard about the witch called Mollie Lee?'

'No — what —'

'Well, they buried her normal like, lying east to west. Mollie Lee, rest in peace. But she wouldn't lie quiet. She just came up and sat on the edge of her grave. Wrapped in her shroud.'

29

'Oooooh — she never —'

'She did. Lots of people seed her. Until the verger said to her — "Mollie Lee," he said, "why can't you lie quiet, like decent folk, why can't you wait for the trumpet till you rise up from your grave?"'

'Oooooh —'

'And she said — I'm a witch, you know I'm a witch and I can't lie quiet until you turn my grave round north to south instead of east to west. That's what Mollie Lee said. North to south. And they did this. And she rested quiet.'

It was true. In Burslem churchyard Mollie Lee's grave lay from north to south. Annie looked when she went to church the next Sunday. It was true. And it was deliciously frightening.

After this she always fled from the old, crooked women who haunted the Five Towns: there were many of them — poor derelicts, battered by poverty, illness, loneliness. And not until she had outgrown her childhood and slept in a bed by herself did she truly enjoy the rousing music of the brass band marching cheerfully down Waterloo Road every Sunday. She had a dread that the dead might mistake those bright trumpets for the last one and heave their skeletons through the sod.

When she was still a child her father fell very ill.

One morning she awoke to hear shouting from his room. His voice, usually so kind, was unrecognizably harsh. Downstairs the kitchen seemed full of white-faced women clasping their hands and stirring pots on the stove.

'It's the crisis,' they told the alarmed child. 'He's delirious.'

She ran out to play. She hopscotched in a safe, side

road and bounced her ball against the high brick wall of a warehouse. Returning a few hours later she found the blinds drawn and the house hushed.

Her mother, almost a stranger behind a mask of haggard, pallid grief, said, 'He's dead!' The ferocious sorrow in her voice terrified the little girl and for the second time that day she escaped, rushing out into the street in a panic, running wildly down the road. As in a nightmare the scene changed for the worse. Familiar doors, with cheeky, snub-nosed handles and smiling letter-box mouths leered at her: invisible hands drew curtains across the windows; the sky turned black. She was outside and alone, excluded from the bright world of home. She had nowhere to go and no one wanted her. In a narrow alley a half-naked child screamed; a drunken man tottered towards her, waving arms like tentacles, and crashed on his face.

Annie never forgot the day her father died.

In those days the loss of the breadwinner was a calamity. Poverty was reckoned to be a real disgrace — a fall from blessedness, an expulsion to the wilderness, a deserved punishment. The spectres of hunger and cold pushed close up outside the windows of the house in Waterloo Road. The iniquitous slums where the great mass of the poor huddled for shelter took on a new sharpness of reality.

The widow dried her tears, drew the curtains across at nightfall, barred the doors and took to making and trimming straw bonnets. By sitting up late at night, working by candlelight, she managed to keep the family just afloat. The elder children left home, scattered to Australia, to America. The younger ones learned the alphabet of economy, learned to do without and be thankful for what they did have. Even eggs, though cheap, were a luxury. As a treat, for high tea on

Sunday, they were allowed half an egg each. By a miracle of resolve, good management and self-sacrifice, the widow managed to get them all to school; she had a deep respect for knowledge and an equally deep loathing of the uncouth mob. When the children were not doing school work they cooked, cleaned, washed, sewed; there was not a minute to spare for idleness and mischief.

Annie, who had many friends and secret sources of food, often wheedled her way out of chores.

'Give you my half-egg if you'll clean the brass for me, Tabby,' she bribed her sister.

Whenever they could they escaped along the towing-paths out into the country. In summer they took picnics and walked all day. They were tremendous walkers and Annie the most tireless of them all. There was always a hill to climb, a corner to turn, a copse to get through, a view to see. Something enchanting beckoned her onwards; she followed eagerly, with no idea of what it was she was always hoping to discover.

Chasing her elusive desires she one day found herself outside a pleasant country house. She had outdistanced the others and stood waiting for them. Out from an open window floated the sound of music — the firm realistic voice of a piano, the alluring, soaring cries of a violin. Never before had she heard anything so beautiful. She was well used to people spanking out jolly tunes on parlour pianos, to brass bands and street musicians begging their way from corner to corner. This music wafting out on to the summer air belonged to a different world. Its loveliness amazed and transfixed her.

A woman looking out of the window saw the untidy, charming girl, garlanded with the daisies, forget-me-nots and other wild flowers she had plucked on the way, gazing up entranced and she said, 'Hullo, who are you? Would you like to come inside and listen to some more music?'

She would have loved to; the sounds ravished her. But reality, in the shape of her boisterous sisters, came dashing up the lane. 'There you are, Annie. You go so fast. Wait for us. Wait —'

Like a wild young animal Annie leapt away from that enchanted house.

'I want to learn music,' she announced when she got home. 'I want to learn properly. I must.'

'I can't afford lessons,' said her mother. 'Later on, perhaps. If you're a good girl and work hard at your lessons at school.'

After that experience Annie's life took on a new dimension: it was as though she had at last found the nourishment for which she had been, almost unknown to herself, obscurely hungering for years. She listened attentively to the music at church, allowing the melodies to impress themselves on her mind and afterwards trying diffidently to re-create them on the old upright piano. When she thought nobody was listening she would sing to herself, sing like an artist disciplining herself, controlling her breath, enlarging her range and volume.

Several times she went back into that part of the country where she had found the house; this time she would go in, boldly knocking at the door. But it was like a lost kingdom of the imagination and she never came across it again.

One Sunday afternoon her mother put on her best clothes, washed her hands in lavender water, cleaned the china ornaments on the piano and said to her children, 'I'm going to get married again.'

'I suppose you ought to be old enough to know your

own mind,' came Annie's swift retort. The news shocked her; she was hurt by her mother's infidelity.

'Don't be so cheeky, child.'

'If I lost *my* husband I should *never* marry again.' said Annie staunchly, faithful to her idea of true love.

'You don't know what you'd do. You're only a child.'

Mr. Bolt, who ran a prosperous little boot and shoe business, moved into their father's empty place. He took them to live in a larger house a little way up the same road and was as kind to them as he knew how.

Good times came again. They had abundant food, could afford to entertain. Annie got her music lessons and went to as many concerts as came her way. She found a real source of joy in music; it steadied and exalted her. She became the star singer in the Band of Hope, that dedicated little group of men and women who fought winter and summer against the menace of drunkenness in the Towns.

> 'My drink is water bright,
> From the crystal spring —'

she sang out, loud and sweet. And the down-trodden men who listened to the pretty, serious girl felt in their hearts that she must be right and they resolved that they would try once more not to succumb to this escape from their harsh lives.

She grew up into a natural beauty, impulsive, untidy, slightly scatty, completely free from vanity, strong as a young lioness, generous as a May morning. She dreamed of leaving the Potteries and travelling to those places about which she had read — Paris, San Francisco, Berlin, Vladivostock. She imagined wearing silk dresses that swept the floor, hats with magnificent plumes; she would be the centre of a group of elegant young men who wore cloaks and had ardent, romantic faces and whose conversation sparkled with poetry and wit. She wanted to go to Weimar and hear the music of the sublime Johann Sebastian played on a German organ. Sometimes, walking along by the canals, she would feel urged to stow herself away on one of the barges, to let herself be carried along willy-nilly through the inland waterways of England and away to the sea and the unknown countries across the horizon. The desire sometimes came so strongly that she had to pick up her skirts and hurry away.

She ran herself up dresses from cheap lengths of material bought in the market, embroidered white collars, fashioned bows for her bonnets, always looked radiant and rather distinguished. People were constantly inviting her to their houses, for parties, homely musical evenings, amateur theatricals. Wherever she went she took with her a rush of vitality, a zestfulness, a loving interest in all the commonplace details of life. Nothing bored her.

At the age of seventeen or eighteen, when she was a pupil teacher, Philip Seabridge began to pay serious court to her. They had known each other as children: his sister was a great friend of Annie — an unusual, carefree girl who tossed off poems, talked most amusingly and shared her love of music and her passion to escape, to travel. Philip Seabridge was an art student, training to be a sculptor, an affectionate, amusing, popular, gifted young man. His hands could create beauty wherever they rested: wherever his eye lingered significant details that had escaped the observation of other people came to light. He had great energy and was interested in everything. He and Annie seemed made for each other and they became engaged. He adored his harum-scarum fiancée, wrote her whimsical love letters, decorating the envelopes with mischievous cupids and bashful postmen, promised her fame, riches, music, the whole wide world.

In 1883 they married. There was trouble in Ireland, and elsewhere, but England was quiet and prosperous and promised to stay so for ever and ever. They came up to London to live and gravitated towards the artists' quarter in Chelsea where they soon found a house. Pip built himself two studios in the long back garden: Annie planted vines, figs, sweet-briars, jasmine and anything else she could beg or buy. They were wonderfully happy together. His work was greatly admired and it seemed as though a future of fame and respect awaited him: people loved Annie for her vivacity and good looks. They soon had a large circle of friends.

Babies came quickly — John, Clara, Bernard, Maud. They had been married for eight years and Joyce was on the way when Pip went down with rheumatic fever. He had never before had a day's illness in his life. In a week he was dead.

As her mother had done before her, Annie dried her tears and considered how she was going to manage. She was rich in happy memories and in friends, but she had absolutely no money at all. She had been a gay, carefree young wife with no notion of domestic economy: Pip had been provider, manager, protector, wishing her to dance along through life enjoying each day to the full.

Some kind friend organized an exhibition of Philip's work; well-known contemporary artists, such as Goscombe John, Wilson Steer, Alfred Gilbert, donated work, here an oil-painting, there a wood-carving, a drawing, a water-colour, a portrait bust. Pip had been loved by his friends and they all wanted to help.

The proceeds from this sale were given to Annie. She paid off the mortgage, let the upper part of the little house, let the two studios at the bottom of the garden. Joyce was born and she settled down in the lower part of the house — two bedrooms, a sitting-room and a kitchen — to struggle against adversity and to bring up the five little ones as well as she could.

CHAPTER THREE

S H E did not marry again.

She was almost a beauty; but she was penniless. And even had a man willing to take on a widow and five little ones presented himself it is doubtful whether she would have accepted him. She would not have found it in her to respond to another man than Philip. He had been so special; they had been so perfectly in tune. Who was there, in the whole world, to measure up to his standards?

Many times her senses deceived her. She thought she heard his voice: she started after strangers in the street, only just managed to stop herself touching a shapely hand that looked familiar.

'There could never be anyone like him again,' she told her mother. 'Never.'

She meant his *look* — that warm, humorous, intent expression. Nobody could have called him a handsome man. But he had this loving, tremendously *alive* look — a radiance, a magnetism.

After this concluding pronouncement she did not ever, all her life, all the long fifty-two years of her widowhood, speak of him again, nor of their years together.

Perhaps she thought, in her simple, practical way, that the past belonged to the past, and was best buried. Perhaps she just could not bring herself to expose her feelings. Silence may have armed her and made the fight just possible.

'You must *eat*,' counselled her mother, who had been through this herself and knew all about the devastating effects of shocked bereavement. 'Eggs are still cheap. And have plenty of liver. And keep a good fire going, darling. You know how the cold makes you feel poorly.'

Probably it was her difficulties that actually saved her. She had no time to brood herself away into a decline. And, basically, she was too healthy to mope. She read through his letters once more, from beginning to end. Then she tied them up with string and pushed them away at the very back of a deep cupboard.

Queen Victoria had not yet spoken her famous words to Balfour. But Annie Seabridge, often ahead of her times, was undoubtedly thinking them well in advance of Victoria Regina: she was not interested in defeat — it did not exist.

Her abundant strength came to her help. She had out-eaten her sisters in youth. Now, in maturity and adversity, she outgrew them in grandeur. Away down that long line of tough old Groves some sturdy shoot must have come to life, the spirit of some wily, gallant spark must have possessed her, as the old gods possessed their Greek heroes. Unsuspected qualities of management and resolve developed in her. She trained her natural impulsiveness to serve her. She studied the comings and goings of luck, learned to wait patiently for opportunities and, when they appeared, to pounce and catch. She hunted bargains, had a flair for recognizing value for money. She charmed gifts from friends and insinuated herself under the skin of certain shop-keepers, who developed a passion for hiding things under the counter, for winking and beckoning to her when the coast was clear. Through the thick and the thin of those hard years she did not lose either her endearing unselfconsciousness — that hall-mark of natural nobility — nor her good looks. And people could not help admiring and doing their best for her.

'Mrs. Seabridge — it's *come* —' and the skinny draper would lean over his counter as though offering a kiss. 'That special roll of flannelette.'

From the secrecy and pride in his voice it might have been a long-lost galleon from the Caribbean.

'I'll measure it. And let you have it. Special price, Mrs. Seabridge, special price — for you. Hush, not a word to anybody!'

Once measured and specially paid for this marvellous bargain would be rushed home, like loot. She would then sit up all night cutting out and sewing — sewing almost as quickly as the machine she could not afford to buy until her real need for it was past — bundling up her babies, making them cosy as beans in a pod.

There were many special godsends. The grocer kept tender bacon pieces for her at only fourpence ha'penny a pound. The greengrocer would let her have the sweet little windfalls for almost nothing, would sell her the heartiest lettuces cheap and would often throw in two or three beetroot for love when he discovered her partiality for this vegetable. Gipsies, migrating up the Thames from the Belvedere marshes, forgot to whine when she appeared at her door enveloped by toddlers and looking rather majestic and sold her clothes' pegs and elastic at bargain prices and swore that good luck was clearly printed on each of the children's right hands. And Annie, seeing the gipsies' rags and their peaked little babies, would dart down the garden where she kept a few hens and return with warm, speckled eggs. Poor as she was, no needy person was pushed from her door: nor did she ever deny food and hospitality to a chance visitor.

She was shaky in her relationship with the Almighty, only went to church for the company and the music, had not the temperament for prayer nor the leisure for meditation: the visible, worrying, human world absorbed her exclusively. Spiritual strength came to her from a small, pure spring of joys. When things started to get beyond her, memories would often well up, would encourage her, decide for her.

One raw winter morning, when two of the children were unwell, she found to her horror that the coal cellar was empty. Since Philip had been snatched from her she had a terror of illness. On this morning, shivering with cold, she was at her wits' end, almost ready to burn all the furniture for fuel. Suddenly she remembered that astonishing, delightful day, years and years ago, when she found she could really skate at last. One friend lent her skates, another flung a red cloak round her shoulders. She hitched up her skirts, slithered out across the frozen canal and then, hey presto, she was going like the wind, the scarlet cloak billowing out like a sail. It was unspeakably thrilling. Time froze like the water; she went on and on. Eventually her anxious friends found her about four miles away, right out in the country, sitting, rosy and untidy, on the bank under a snow-covered alder.

This recollection called forth a new surge of energy and optimism. She threw on her coat, seized the pram and rushed out through the stinging air from friend to friend, borrowing and pleading until she had enough coal to warm the house.

Lying awake, worrying about the enormous future, about how to equip the children to cope with a life that was all too often starkly indifferent to frail flesh and blood, that idyllic house in the country came back to her with the force of a revelation. That house with the open window through which music had poured out over her, like a blessing — that house she had not been able to find again, that might almost have been a dream. Of course! She would re-create that lost inspiration. Now, when all the papers were talking about the discordant clashing of Imperial forces on the continents of Africa and Asia, she would teach her children the elements of divine harmony. With the help of music she would create a little sanctuary, here, in the crowded Chelsea sitting-room with its matting on the floor, its bobble-fringe on the mantelpiece, its strong sofa that stood up to any amount of children's bounding and scrapping, its worn wicker chairs that contributed to the conversation with critical creaks and excited squeaks.

Music, the refiner, the redeemer — music that could, and *would*, lift them out of the rut of poverty, bear them up and away from the common dross. The children should all become musicians: there should be a whole family of them, like the Bachs.

When it was discovered that they had, in fact, all been born with perfect pitch and were quite incapable of singing out of tune her enthusiasm threatened to assume the proportions of folly. They should be opera singers, virtuoso violinists. As a start they would at least be able to take part in those musical evenings, organized by some of her friends, that were the social highlight of her present life.

She could not afford to buy toys for them, but she did

manage to rake together a collection of stringed instruments. She willed and charmed the old upright piano in the Waterloo Road to move south from Burslem; it came at her bidding.

The children began to learn the realities of a life that had no balancing father, that was dominated by an impulsively ambitious mother, who lived more by vision and intuition than by reason. They had to spend *hours* a day practising; it was their only amusement. As they grew older she even made them stay at home from school in the afternoons so that they could do their scales and five-finger exercises. The little house resounded with scrapings and sawings and strummings, an endless succession of chords, arpeggios, pizzicatos. It was murder for the people in the other half of the house. And for the children it was often hell.

Joyce started running away to find a better life directly she could run. At the age of two she was already asking for her hat and taking herself off. The first time she was found by the police toddling round Sloane Square, a mile away; another time they found her sturdily crossing Battersea Bridge, and yet another hovering outside Battersea Dogs' Home. By the age of four, however, she, too, had a fiddle under her chin and was playing passages here and there in the Seabridge sextet — Annie at the old upright piano and the rest of them bowing and sawing.

On very busy days, on washing day for instance, they all had to get up early and do their practice before breakfast. Often she would make time to stand over them, rapping their knuckles when they lagged and fumbled: on their good days, however, grandiose dreams possessed her — she saw them capturing the hearts of the *élite* in every European capital, she saw her beloved John enthroned on the organ in St.

43

Paul's, thundering out the *St. Matthew Passion* and lovely Maud, the prima donna, being showered with roses as she took curtain after curtain at the Garden.

'I saw a harmonium in the King's Road the other day, Johnnie. You could practise on that. For a start.'

'But the money, Mother!' protested John, who would much rather have had a magnifying glass, or a magnet. 'The *money*.'

He and Clara, the two eldest, knew too much about the inside story of financial strain and torment for them ever to be easy when it came to spending money. They knew the wakeful nights, the pale mornings, the anguished calculations that went wrong, the weeks and weeks of stinting and then, when their mother could stand the strain no longer, a shattering outburst of extravagance, a catharsis of the purse. And then back to a period of Staffordshire oatcakes and the severe tick-tock of the metronome.

'If I'm very careful for the next few weeks I think we could manage it. Your future's worth making sacrifices for, Johnnie. The family won't mind living on oatcakes. Where's Clara? *Clara* —'

So Clara sighed and obediently did her duty, soaking oatmeal in water, adding flour and mixing to the consistency of cream, cooking flat cakes on a hot, greased girdle and then frying them in the generous fat from the fourpence ha'penny a pound bacon pieces and piling them up on dishes.

In small amounts they were delicious: too many cloyed and bored.

When Annie went out to buy the harmonium, found it beyond her means and came home with pounds of extra butter, yards of material to make dresses for the girls and with nothing for him John silently registered a vow that one day soon he would take over the financial reins. Stealthily he started to plan and to calculate.

The practising continued. As well as music they were all learning obedience, concentration, persistence, discipline.

Even so, young flesh could not stand it indefinitely. There were revolts.

'I won't, I won't, I won't —' Bernard, a very shy, difficult little boy, staged one of his strikes. He had been up-graded to the cello and could hardly get the pot-bellied thing between his legs.

'How dare you, my son! Go on playing! At once!'

'I won't, I won't —' Bernard, forcing himself to be brave, armed himself with passive resistance and threw himself flat on the floor.

'Leave him alone,' conceded Annie, when she saw he meant it. 'He'll soon be tired of such naughtiness.'

'Run away with me,' he implored Maud next day. 'We'll dig a hole through the centre of the earth and go to Australia. Come on. We'll find *gold* in Australia. *Please*.'

Maud put on her best dress and went to the end of the garden with him. Bernard's will was steely. The spade, however, capitulated, refusing to penetrate the London gravel.

Maud fancied herself as a harpist. When this whim was denied her she lost interest in music and contrived, by means of pretended headaches, to do the minimum. She laid her pale, slim hands on her forehead, simulated elegant languors. It nearly always worked.

'Doesn't my pet feel well this afternoon? Sit over there, in the corner instead and practise your *Gentle Jesus*. You can recite it by heart, now, can't you?'

Over there, in the corner, hung a mirror. Her reflection made her feel better at once and she mouthed the words with gusto.

'Gentle Jesus, meek and mild,
Dum-di-dum a little child —'

It didn't really matter what she said. Clara was creating such a splendid furore on the piano that nobody would notice her gentle little Jesus.

Clara had loyally immersed herself in this business of music. Perhaps more than the others she really understood her mother's trials and courage and wanted to help and to please her. She plunged valiantly into the whirling keys and chords, the chromatic scales, the descending fifths and thirds, and she emerged from the ordeal a true musician. She could play Brahms and Beethoven: she could make her mother cry with her interpretations of Chopin. ('Chopin' onions again, Mother?' Bernard would remark with precocious wit, when emotion gushed from Clara's fingers and his mother's eyes). She was mistress not only of the piano, but of strings as well.

'Di-da, di-da —' went on Maud, keeping time with the majestic beat of Beethoven. 'Pity mice implicitly.' She had no idea what *implicitly* meant: but about mice she knew a great deal too much. Unable to decide which was worse — the quivering, scuttling, thieving creatures, or the *snap* in the night as that awful trap caught another victim, she turned to the mild Jesus. Pity them, Lord, pity the mice.

It was years before she learned the correct words.

In spite of the earnest, talkative Socialists of the nineteenth century, to be poor in those *fin-de-siècle* days was still a disgrace. Whatever might be the cause of material distress the stark fact remained — it was some-

46

thing of which to be deeply ashamed. The poor meant the great unwashed, meant reeking slums, crime, squalor unlimited, meant a degenerate character, rags, bare feet, disease, gin palaces. Therefore, if misfortune had squeezed you out of a comfortable life into strait circumstances, you washed yourself with fastidious care, you scrubbed and polished your home, you dressed with immaculate taste, set your sights on a starry future and worked like a slave to get there, and you never, never let anyone know how poor you were. It was a curious masque of deception, really, because all one's acquaintances and friends must have known. However, the rules of the game said one must pretend they didn't know, one must pretend that everything was all right.

Domestic labour was so cheap in those times that to be servantless was to be right at the bottom of the social scale. Chores had to be done secretly, first thing in the morning, or last thing at night. No one must know. Should that apparition of doubtful charm, the Unexpected Visitor, pop in when the family was occupied with housework Maud, who always managed to look dazzlingly unruffled because she always contrived to do the least work, would be left to hold the fort while the others vanished into the bedroom in a scamper of consternation to titivate and change. Although Annie was known as a notorious bargain-hunter, an eccentric borrower of coal, it probably never occurred to anyone that her doorstep was kept spotless by a dead of night scrub.

Holidays were something other people had. There were long walks in the Parks and along by the Thames, and visits to relations, but not proper holidays. One parched summer the breeze shook five whole pounds from somewhere — five golden sovereigns. That summer the heat was choking and the air in the house

47

stagnant with flies. Annie decided to take them all to Worthing.

This momentous week was not entirely successful. They had not enough money left over for swimming things after their board and lodging was paid for and they had to bathe in their underclothes. The girls cringed and blushed. Bernard, feeling sick with embarrassment, would only paddle. He drew pictures of boats on every scrap of paper he could lay hands on, fashioned barques and wind-jammers out of sand, giving them tamarisk twigs for masts and scraps of seaweed for flags, and he stared out across the lukewarm Channel with furious resolve in his heart. The sea called to him, the gulls and the wind and the horizon called; he mapped out his future, believing the day would soon come when he would set off, like all younger sons, to seek and to find his fortune.

This game of illusion and reality, this continual pretence, this early domination by an implacably ambitious mother created in all the children a curious mixture of inferiority and superiority, as well as a prudence in money matters that sometimes amounted to stinginess.

They had the natural superiority born of health and strength, of respectable ancestors, of family love — the superiority of clear intelligence, of considerable talents and gifts, of bravely facing up to life's many challenges. They looked rather distinguished, too. Appearances meant a great deal to Annie, who had innately good taste and the inherited skill of many generations in her fingers. Although the cost to her meant long nights of needlework and days of eating mainly oatcakes, she would never allow them to wear cheap and nasty clothes. They were always well dressed, with style, care and a certain charming originality. The inferiority came because they imagined society despised

48

them, because they felt they were being crushed down into a class where they did not really belong, because they obscurely felt they were somehow to blame for being poor. The two boys, especially, were to work all their life as though possessed by daemons, aiming at goals that always receded. All their lives they were to strive both to fulfil their mother's expectations of them, and to justify themselves before society, making up for the tough start destiny had double-dealt them.

The same sort of superiority–inferiority complex was to be repeated, more gently and with different variations, in the following generation. In most cases the conundrum was to be satisfactorily worked out: but in one case the pattern smudged and darkened and led to tragedy.

The boys were good scholars. Round the corner, at the College of St. Mark, they were crammed with knowledge. Before they were even thirteen their flexible minds were stretched to take in (and retain) Chemistry, practical and theoretical Physics, Euclid, Trigonometry, Latin, French, German, Economics, and all the other usual subjects. Not for them, however, the sauntering home in the afternoon to practise. For them school all day, homework at night and up in the morning early to practise. It was a hard life. But they grew strong to meet its demands, and they had the security that comes from an affectionate and happy family relationship, from one hundred per cent loyalty to their mother, from a united struggle to better themselves.

And they had their escape routes.

John could always lose himself among the waves of air, among currents of electricity and the primordial power of lightning. His half of the chest of drawers shared with Bernard was a jumble of wires, screws, lenses culled from all over the place, scraps of magnetic iron, tiny phials containing mysterious powders. He examined mousetrap cheese and rain water under a magnifying glass, read everything he could about wireless, started to make a receiving set and dreamed Faustian dreams of power and infinite knowledge. He would have been prepared to swop his young soul for a set of *Encyclopaedia Britannica* had Mephistopheles come his way.

For Bernard it was the waves on the water that lured him, the sweep of the Thames at the bottom of the street, the boats with their alert sails and dizzy masts, the glamorous cargoes waiting shipment to the Far East or the Wild West. In leisure moments at home he would cover pages and pages with quick, sure drawings of his nautical observations. From there it was a small step to do quick portraits, to dash off funny sketches for the amusement of anyone who needed cheering up. Artist friends of the family would glance at him as he sat drawing and would murmur, 'Ah — he has the real touch — yes, he has the power of the line — his father's spirit —' Bernard had no idea what these cryptic remarks meant. Nor had he any inkling of the trap he was so innocently setting for himself.

When he was old he would reply to inquisitive people in that quiet, beautiful voice of his, 'Had things been different I might now be a retired Admiral. But I was always destined to be an artist. The family circle consisted almost entirely of writers and artists and musicians and no other career was ever considered possible for me.'

When he was young, however, he put up a good struggle.

'I won't, I won't, I won't be an artist!' he announced when the news was broken that the honour of following in his father's footsteps was to be his. 'I don't want to go to Art School. I tell you, I *won't*.'

'It's naughty to be obstinate,' cajoled his mother.

'I want to be a sailor. I *will* go to sea.'

'You *will* go to Art School,' replied his mother with the mildness that springs from absolute certainty. And she went on making arrangements, pulling strings.

'I'm going across the Atlantic. Round Cape Horn. I'm going to force a passage through the Bering Strait in winter. I want to be becalmed in the Persian Gulf.'

'As a hobby, love. When you're a famous sculptor.'

Poor Bernard — it was useless. Not only was his destiny pressing in on him; it was also found that he was short-sighted.

Later on, when fame brushed his shoulder, he could afford his adventurous hobby. He raced International dinghies, he cruised round the coasts of Scandinavia, he even toured the Mediterranean in a battleship. Once, it is true, he did manage to work his passage to America on a cattle ship; but that was not quite the same thing as serving in the Senior Service.

So to Art School he went, at the age of about twelve, to the original School of Arts and Crafts, somewhere near Langham Place, two or three evenings a week, as well as his normal school work and up in the morning early-O to practise music. He was still young enough to be nervous coming home alone in the dark: so to keep up his courage he would whip his top all the way down Regent Street to Piccadilly, where he could relax in the safety of the old horse bus.

When John was fourteen or fifteen and his mother went out one morning with the week's housekeeping to shop for necessities and came back saying 'I've put down a deposit for a second-hand Bechstein Grand. Now your voice has broken you deserve a fine piano. Aren't we lucky? We'll manage to pay for it somehow.' — the diffident boy became a man. He told her it was nonsense to go on and on like this about music. Yes, they did all have perfect pitch and were all fairly musical. But they'd never shake the world. *He* was going to devote himself to electricity: this was the hope and the power of the future. *He* was going to take over the family finances immediately. They must give up thinking they could get by on oatcakes. The girls must never, never again have to bathe in their vests.

Annie gave in without a murmur. The ability to adapt herself quickly to overwhelming changes was one of the characteristics of her lively nature. Johnnie's new strength and insistence thrilled her. Her doting became idolatry.

The money situation steadied and gradually improved. John acquired cunning and started to develop uncommon abilities: he was to grow into one of those rare men who did not merely earn money but *made* it. He wisely never disclosed the secrets of his alchemy. In later years his wife, Mollie, when pushed to extremes by his insults, would bellow: 'I know enough about you, you old so-and-so, to send you to prison for the rest of your so-and-so life.' John, however, would merely laugh at her, his clever, loud laugh, and go on eating shrimps.

Under his command everyone received regular pocket money as payment for their share of the chores. He allocated it according to his estimate of merit: Maud, who did least work, got most money because she was the prettiest. Maud also found she could wheedle extra money out of Joyce by pretending to be ill, even dying. Joyce, flooded even then with the milk of human kindness, did not have it in her to refuse her sister's last gasps for money. 'If you could — just let — me — have — another shilling — I'm sure I'd — recover —' Beauty is rarer even than gratitude, more precious than honour; Maud naturally made the most of her advantages. It said much for family unity and affection that no one really minded or thought it unfair.

Annie was never to realize her girlhood ambition to hear Bach played on a German organ in Weimar. But she did hear *The Ring* sung by Germans in Karlsruhe.

Britain was strengthening and extending Imperial responsibilities. The Seabridges were enlarging their interests and requirements. Johnnie had irrevocably decided on his electrical engineering. Clara (alas, the only one) seemed bent on a musical career. Although Germany and England were not on the best of terms the Vaterland remained the most musical country in Europe; and Germany also possessed the best technical and scientific colleges in the world.

Annie pondered, tossed and turned at night, consulted her friends, tried to take everything into consideration, as everyone said she should, hesitated — and then with the fearlessness that is born of devotion she packed the family's clothes and shepherded all the children on to a slow boat for Rotterdam. From there they dawdled up the Rhine to Mannheim and so on to the pretty town of Karlsruhe. All town-planning students knew that city with its streets radiating like a fan from the Grand Ducal Palace in the centre, a quiet, sleepy, most attractive place: the arcaded streets with striped sentry boxes here and there were comparatively deserted and an atmosphere of calmness reigned everywhere.

It was the first time Annie had left England. She did not understand more than a few words of German. Politics had always largely passed her by and she was unaware of the fact that a nasty wave of anti-British feeling was rolling round Germany.

As they explored Karlsruhe, all six of them in a bunch, looking for a cheap, unfurnished flat, people pointed and made hostile remarks.

'Mother, Mother —' the two boys had learned German at school — 'they're jeering at us. Let's go back to England.'

'Nonsense!' She was getting rather short-sighted. 'They're admiring the girls' looks, of course.' She graciously nodded to the sneering groups and went on her flat-hunting way.

The gods love the gallant and, faith being invincible, she found her cheap, unfurnished flat. She bought bits and pieces from junk shops and the boys knocked together benches and tables from orange boxes. The Germans' wounded pride healed and letters poured in addressed to *The Lovely Ladies Seabridge*. They went to the Opera two or three times a week. They tried to read Goethe, Schiller, Heine, Hegel. The girls attended school and began to speak excellent German. John did brilliantly at the Technical College. Bernard was so difficult that he was sent home to live with relations and to begin his full-time training as a sculptor: he was barely fourteen.

A soothsayer in the Black Forest dealt cards and foretold that Clara would not go back to England when the others did. Clara did not. She adventurously answered an advertisement for a violinist to go to Italy and live with a husband (cello) and wife (piano) on the shores of Lake Garda. She seemed to have inherited Annie's fearlessness; although only sixteen, she arrived alone in Milan at night and somehow found her way to the villa by the Lake. There she spent two interesting years playing trios. She might have stayed longer had not the Frau grown jealous of her clever, adopted daughter who could not only play the fiddle well, but could also play the piano much better than she could.

All back in England again, life blossomed.

John moved them from the half-house in Chelsea to a whole house in Putney. With him trained and earning, with Bernard, though still a student, getting a few commissions and with Clara able to give music lessons to help her through the Royal College of Music Maud could be sure of staying safely on at the Slade and Joyce could finish her schooling, could matriculate and perhaps even get to a University.

The struggle of bringing them all up on nothing seemed suddenly to end. Annie became as merry as a skyful of larks. Men who had admired her spirit and her appearance *en passant* while the children were young and hungry now stopped and took a closer look and found she was still good-looking and had remarkable vitality. But it is doubtful if she gave any of them a second, or even a first, thought. She was, by now, so completely wrapped up in her children that nothing else really registered. She experienced life through them, allowed them to carry her along on contemporary currents.

Invitations rushed in on her. She always accepted. She was known to make an instant recovery and rise up from her sick bed should an unexpected invitation come when she was unwell. She was known to eat so much at certain receptions that she was literally unable to rise from the table. People went on asking her: she was original, she was decorative, she was funny.

Yes, life was suddenly lovely. It was full of boats, bicycles, new friends, outings, musical evenings, sing-songs, masques, picnics, parties, parties, parties. Oh, that it could have lasted for ever, that state of perma-nent felicity, with the family cemented round her in love and loyalty.

But she had read the poems of Blake and knew she must kiss the joys as they flew. Close behind came other winged joys to be greeted, came Cupid to enlarge the family circle — Maud's handsome painter, Reggie, Clara's kind, funny Salisbury, Bernard's lovely Dorothy with her flashing moods and sparkling graces, Joyce's debonair Roy.

She did not, however, kiss John's Irish Mollie.

She disliked the buxom, talkative young woman on sight. So did Clara, Maud and even Joyce. They were to dislike her all their lives and never to forgive her for marrying John. She was everything they had worked so hard not to be. Mollie, they said, was common, was brash, had obscure origins — no rampant lions or fess-wise bundles in her pedigree.

'Her people probably come from the Irish bogs,' tittered Maud.

'She smells', said Annie anxiously, 'as though she'd just come out of a pub.'

Collectively and separately they discouraged their brother.

'She's so greedy,' said Clara. 'She pushes down her food in a disgusting manner.'

'She has no education,' commented Joyce. 'And quite unmusical.'

'She's unrefined,' they all complained. 'She's not a lady, She's *common*.'

But Mollie was already John's mistress when he introduced her to the family. She adored him, ministered to his physical needs, probably understood him well, and, although he often treated her badly, she never let him go: and after his death she only managed to survive one sodden, muddled year. People said he had picked her up in a pub in Liverpool. People said her morals were non-existent and that John would have been much happier and better off without her. But who knows? People's deepest needs are often mysterious and the ways of fate are strange and hard to fathom.

One after the other they all married and for a time they were all happy, in their own ways.

Nineteen-fourteen brought Bernard post-haste back from Italy where he was completing his long, fourteen-year training, having won the double honour of the Royal Academy Travelling Scholarship and the First Rome Scholarship. It transformed John, who had gone to Russia on engineering business, into a diplomat: he was appointed British Consul in Moscow and later had to run for his life across the immense Siberian wastes with Mollie, with Mollie's fur coat and tea-pot and with all their memories of pre-Revolutionary splendours.

Bernard returned to Italy to serve among the murderous, shrapnel-splintered Alps. Reggie and the others waded into that hell of mud and carnage in France. The young mothers at home with their babies (Diana, Sarah, Betty, Deborah) endured and tried not to think too much.

When Roy was killed in one of those obscene slaughters of 1916 Annie did something very unusual. She opened a deep drawer and from the back pulled out the thin bundle of her husband's letters. One of these she gave to Joyce, silently pointing to a passage written in strong, flowing handwriting. The young woman read:

E   57

'What trials we have gone through — and are still going through, heavy enough to bear they are and yet surely they will be for our good, if we have only patience enough to seek out the lessons they ought to teach us. In my better moments I firmly believe that the true philosophy of life consists in living earnestly every moment of our existence, whether the sun is shining brightly on us, or the sky is thick with clouds.'

Joyce read those homely words from the father she had never known, then folded the letter again and gave it back without a word. Some time later she said: 'That makes three generations of us, Mother. Perhaps there was a curse, or something. Like a Greek tragedy.'

'You must marry again.' implored her mother, who had not studied Greek tragedy and saw only her daughter's great need. 'I shall pray you will.'

During the following years, before Joyce was lucky enough to happen on another love, mother and daughter were very close. Joyce, the youngest, petted and adored in childhood, now gave this back in threefold devotion. She had a good job, at the School of Oriental Studies, and out of her earnings bought many small luxuries. She bought a motor-cycle and toured England with her mother in the side-car, she took her on continental holidays and even managed to buy her, at last, a Bechstein Grand.

CHAPTER FOUR

SUMMER was at its most beautiful: Sarah's birthday
was drawing near again.

A cornucopia must have poured out its blessings
over her. Beautiful, laughing Sarah made, from her first
day, good entrances at good times. She came in June,
when the world was full of flowers and juicy fruits, of
sunshine, birds' songs, the scent of honeysuckle and
roses and syringa. Things always arranged themselves
to Sarah's advantage. Nor was she mean with her good
luck; she always tried to share her bounty.

Her birthday party was a day the cousins looked forward to for weeks, a day to emblazon in their diaries. It
never seemed to rain, they could have it out in Granny's
garden, they could eat as many strawberries as they
wanted — eat till they bust. On this day Granny's
maxim — 'Better belly bust than good food be lost!' —
almost came true.

Like Christmas, Easter, fireworks, this was an annual
occasion, an excuse for a party, a reason for Granny to
insist on a family gathering.

She was living in Oxford Road, Putney, now, in a
pretty, double-fronted house with a fair-sized garden

that appeared enormous to the grandchildren. John had ensconced her here early in the 1920's and he and Bernard each gave her an allowance. John's contribution was very handsome; his sisters were delighted and amazed at such uncharacteristic generosity. After Granny's death, when it was discovered that clever John had been buying the house for himself by means of her monthly mortgage payments they were understandably shocked by this double-dealing but had to admit to each other — 'Well, what could you expect — John never gave anyone anything in his life —'

The house was roomy and the upper floor was converted into a self-contained flat. At various times various members of the family inhabited it; Granny could not bear to be alone. Maud and Reggie were there for a few years: Joyce and Angus moved in and out several times. Dorothy said 'No, certainly not! I shouldn't dream of it!' but occasionally coveted in her heart those light and airy rooms. For the last two or three years Johnnie had found it convenient to move himself and Mollie into the house. They existed in an uneasy *ménage à trois* and Johnnie, torn between idolizing mother and adoring wife, was finding it increasingly necessary to seek peace and solace elsewhere in order to keep himself sane. He went abroad on business as much as possible. Mollie tried to go with him as often as she could: when this was out of the question she comforted herself in sundry ways that appalled the family. John brought home all sorts of exciting things from his foreign trips — scientific instruments from Germany, the latest domestic gadgets, books on sculpture for Bernard. He also brought back photographs of a slender, attractive young woman called Annabella, who, he said, lived in Vienna with her parents and sang Viennese songs in a quite delightful manner. Her parents always welcomed him with good, homely Austrian cooking and light native wine. These photographs sent Mollie into a blind rage of jealousy — she would storm, swear and weep herself scarlet and puffy.

Apart from the abomination of Mollie, for whose downfall she never ceased to wish, Granny was very happy in Oxford Road. She filled the large, light rooms with flowers, pictures, children and the garden with colour, scent, mystery, joy and a strong, creaking swing.

In her role of grandmother she flowered prodigiously. She was mad about the grandchildren, absolutely obsessed. Maud had her bewitchingly lovely Sarah; Clara had Betty and Deborah, neat and sweet as cherubs; Bernard had his three golden-haired darlings, Diana, dainty as a princess, Vicky, the quaint little tomboy, Ralph, quick and merry as sunshine; and Joyce, happily married for the second time to Angus, had her heavenly screaming rascals, Bruce and Jocelyn.

Her lap was brimming over, her life as golden as ripe corn. She felt mighty as a spreading oak, benevolently protective, invincible in herself. Not even Mollie rearranging all the furniture and shrieking blue murder at John could ruffle her serenity when the grandchildren played roly-poly down the grassy bank, or hunted the thimble among the Staffordshire figures and Tauchnitz editions in the drawing-room.

She had been happy enough in those pre-war years, before war and marriage had seized up her treasures one by one, taking them into secluded regions of dreams and nightmares where she could not follow. But as a grandmother she was completely fulfilled. That incredible energy still blazed. She still sewed like an express train, never went anywhere without taking knitting or crochet, even to evening receptions, always did several things at once, invariably said 'Yes' to invitations, climbed into bed for an afternoon cat-nap and then went on without stopping till after midnight. But, no longer fed by necessity, the flames of energy were gentler. At the rare times she suffered from over-tiredness and depression she would, despite the anti-drink crusading of her youth, revive herself with a nip of 'medicinal' brandy.

Yes, she grew into an archetypal grandmother, a classical, memorable figure. When women moved their skirts up above their knees and cropped their hair to look like boys, Granny's skirts still reached her ankles. Her only concession to fashion was to smooth away her girlish, untidy fringe and move her nut-brown bun forward into two coils round her ears. She was large, voluminously robed, immensely broad in the beam, a symbol of comfort — handing out syrup of figs to the constipated, dabs of vaseline to the spotty, warm infusions of blackcurrants to the sleepless, body belts to the babies. Should the day be chilly and the fire low there was no one who could produce warmth like she could — a few lumps of coal placed deftly here and there, a good puff from her strong lungs, and the flames leapt up like hungry tigers. She could, in the twinkling of an eye, fling various ingredients into a bowl, bang them about with a wooden spoon and produce knobs of fudge as smooth as dark velvet, or creamy slabs of exquisitely melting peppermint. And out in the garden, where everything grew in charming profusion, it seemed that she had only to jab withered sticks into the earth for them to be almost instantly dotted all over with green buds again. Vicky, an avid reader of fairy stories, believed she chanted spells over the sticks, or sat at the Bechstein on moonlit nights playing suitable music. The other grandchildren knew it was just the power and prerogative of all true grandmothers — fertility, cosiness, food, plants, fudge, syrup of figs, children.

As her fifteenth birthday approached, Sarah started to lay aside childish ways for ever. She would soon be well on the way to twenty, growing up to be the great and gracious lady she felt to be her inevitable destiny. She stopped bouncing and bounding, and began to move with supple grace. She racked and twisted her luxuriant hair into kiss curls, smarming them down like a film star. She did not laugh less, but her laughter contained exciting depths and innuendos — almost as if she knew more than she should. She discovered that her huge, dark eyes could beckon and entice. Men turned round to look after her. Her mother had sleepless nights worrying. Granny was tremendously proud. The younger cousins were full of admiration; the older ones occasionally felt twinges of envy. She had *everything*.

One afternoon, when all the cousins had for some reason or other converged on Oxford Road, she summoned Diana, Betty and Deborah down to the corner of the garden. Vicky, who was always somewhere else — driving the milkman's horse, or making friends with tramps, or reading her eyes out — was not included. She heard about the conference afterwards and did as her sister told her.

'This year I'm getting underclothes with real lace on them', said Sarah, leading the way down the garden.

She waited for the murmurs of envy that were her due. They came and she went on playing to a captive audience.

'And Mummy's giving me a Morny compact!'

'Lucky pig!' said Betty.

'Oh —' sighed Diana, 'oh — how I wish Mummy approved of make-up —'

'Powder's not make-up, silly. Powder's an essential.'

'Even powder makes Mummy cross. She says it spoils me. I have to do it in secret.'

'And I'm, getting a pair of *proper*, high-heeled court shoes,' went on Sarah. 'I'll be able to make that lovely tapping sound on the pavement. So important! Everyone'll hear me coming now!'

'Swank pot!' said Betty.

Sarah laughed happily. 'Never mind! You'll soon be fifteen. And this year I've decided — I've decided that instead of a party —'

She pushed past a bush of syringa and the petals showered down on her hair like confetti.

'— anyway, I'll tell you what I've decided when we're properly in the corner.'

The corner was always reserved for special conversations. Here they made plans, exchanged confidences, swapped knowledge about sex. From this corner Betty was sent to look up 'sperm whales' in Uncle John's *Encyclopaedia Britannica*; to this corner she returned wondering what on earth the connection could be.

It was a fascinating corner. Into the mound of soft earth Granny had jabbed cuttings from currant bushes brought back from her trip to Moscow when John was important there. And lying about between these spicy bushes were the remains of their grandfather's work — crumbling plaster casts of classical figures, of heads, hands and strong thighs — with which Granny had never been able to bring herself to part. 'Break them up!' artist friends advised. 'He would have wished you to do so.' To her this would have been like destroying a priceless image of the truth. So they kept her company, moving house whenever she did, a gathering of gentle ghosts that became dustier and more fragile as the years weathered them — as mutely alive as those words about the past that were never spoken. The grandchildren thought they were interesting and rather funny: they practised kissing on Apollo's plaster lips, they held hands with Mercury.

The corner had further charms. Here the ground was higher than in the rest of the garden and here, half-hidden among the currant bushes and the plaster casts, they could look over into the forbidden, next-door garden and bait the three girls they were not allowed to have anything to do with — Beryl, Elsa and 'Ilda. They were common children. *Common* was the worst adjective Granny knew; it meant the outposts of hell, the abasement of the human spirit. Beryl, Elsa and 'Ilda spoke with *common* accents, dressed in nasty, *common*, mass-produced clothes, played in a *common* garden. It often hurt Granny, looking out from an upstairs window, to think that this garden could exist side by side with hers; it was an unmerited social injustice. There the flowers were planted out in prim, mingy clumps, dots of daisies, dabs of zinnias and begonias, stunted privet bushes set in diamond-shaped patches on the grass. Whereas on Granny's side of the wall there were luxuriantly bold Impressionistic sloshes and splodges of poppies, marigolds, irises, lupins, of spicy herbs, of hyssop burdened with bees, of balsam ejecting seeds with impatient lust should even a butterfly's wing chanced to brush them.

It was no wonder that Granny strictly forbade the children to communicate. And it was no wonder that the children got a thrill out of secretly disobeying her injunctions.

'Yes, this year,' said Sarah, her arm round Mercury's

waist, 'this year I've decided to sacrifice my party. 'I'm not going to have a party.'

'*Not?*' Diana felt the sacrifice would be hers. She was longing for those strawberries and cream.

'What are you sacrificing it for?' Betty controlled her emotions in the interests of cool logic.

'For Lily Longton.'

'Oh, *her*.'

Sarah's social conscience was developing by fits and starts: now and then she took up causes with enthusiasm. Lily Longton was a cause — a pale, deprived child who lived in a basement near Putney Bridge, a child too poor to be common.

'The poor child — do you know —', Sarah, a natural orator, began building up sympathy for the cause —, 'she has to wear cast-offs —'

'*Cast-offs!*'

They, daughters of artists one and all, had to endure the embarrassment of individually designed, uncommon clothes such as skirts made from curtains, or oatmeal-coloured material draped round them like Greek tunics. But never cast-offs. Such clothes were worse than rags. They didn't fit properly, they had a lingering smell of other people about them. Ugh, poor Lily Longton! How humiliating!'

Sarah waited for the wild murmurs to die down before playing her next trick.

'And do you know what she has for tea? Every day for tea?'

'Tadpoles!' suggested Deborah wildly. The only time she had seen this Lily Longton the wispy girl had been carrying a jar full of frog spawn from a pond on the Common. All the points seemed to add up to some such diet.

'For her tea,' went on Sarah, calmly ignoring this

shot in the dark, 'she has bread and dripping. Every day.'

'I love dripping,' said Betty, beginning to feel irritated. 'I adore the luscious jelly from the meat at the bottom.'

'This sort of dripping hasn't got jelly from the meat. You buy it from the butcher in a cold, greasy slab.'

'Well?' Betty resented her cousin's cool bossiness.

'Well?' Sarah waited with quiet confidence.

'There must be something we could do. Buy her something —' murmured Diana uneasily.

'*Exactly!*' Sarah smiled triumphantly, a committee woman winning a decisive point in a debate. 'But first we need money. To buy her clothes. And butter.'

'Perhaps an art exhibition?' This was the only serious way of making money that Diana knew about.'

'No, not an art exhibition.' Sarah had worked out all the details days ago. 'We're going to have a bazaar.' She looked at her cousins' glum faces and laughed. 'Cheer up! It'll be fun.'

'What'll we sell?' asked Diana anxiously. 'Will we have to buy what we sell first? To sell it after, I mean?' Money was a lasting worry at home. Her mother's purse always looked so flat. They had to be careful what they bought — only necessities, no luxuries. Sometimes the parents quarrelled about money, spitting out bitter, frightening words at each other.

'Yes, what?' echoed Betty crossly. She was fed up. It was jolly well time old Sarah stopped thinking she could tell them all what to do — she was always pushing them around to do something, acting plays, producing magazines, creating ballets — 'What?'

'You are a dreary lot,' said Sarah, temporarily defeated. 'Really selfish. Don't you ever feel *guilty* when you're wearing gorgeous new clothes and someone like poor Lily has to put on — yes, even has to put on other people's *knickers*. Don't you?'

'Let's start making plans,' announced Betty firmly, won over.

'Good.' Sarah had her plans ready. 'I shall have the Arts and Crafts stall. Diana, you do food. Your mother'll help you with the cooking. And Betty and Deborah, you can have the White Elephant stall.'

Betty's mouth fell open.

'I've got lots of ideas for my stall,' went on Sarah hastily, not caring for the look of stupefied fury on Betty's face. 'Earrings out of buttons, and rag dolls, and — oh yes, Vicky'd better do something. What about books for her? You'll tell her, won't you, Diana? And any pictures she can find.'

'What exactly is a White Elephant stall?' Betty managed to ask.

'Isn't it a gorgeous name?' laughed Sarah, not knowing how to explain.

'What?' Betty refused to be charmed.

'Oh well — you know —'

'We *refuse* to have the White Elephant stall. Don't we, Deborah?'

Deborah, who had lost the thread since her tremendous imaginative outburst of *tadpoles*, said yes, no, they would. Actually she was just then intensely interested in bigger fish than Lily Longton. She had caught a glimpse of a checked cotton dress over the wall, had discerned the squeak of a patent leather ankle-strap shoe. She dug her nails into the crumbling mortar between the bricks and strained up to see more.

'*We* shall have the BetDeb stall,' announced Betty haughtily.

'What on earth's that?' laughed Sarah.

'Wait and see.' Betty had no idea herself what it would be.' 'Deborah, what are you doing?'

Wordless with excitement Deborah pointed to Beryl, Elsa and 'Ilda mincing down their prim garden path.

The doubts and resentments of Sarah's bazaar vanished. Family cocksureness and a traditional conceit united them. They tensed themselves for attack.

'Co — look at 'er shoes. Don't they look *common?*' Betty loosed the first dart.

'Can see those sorta dresses anywhere,' carried on Sarah. 'Ever so cheap. Ten a penny.'

'They cost me Mum five bob in the market,' retaliated battling 'Ilda.

'Wouldn't be seen dead in the fings you 'ave to wear,' added Beryl.

The delicious verbal battle had been waging at least ten bloody minutes when Clara, always the first with extra-sensory perceptions when the honour of her daughters was endangered, glanced out of the drawing-room window. She was displeased by what she saw.

'Children, children — what are you doing?' She pushed her way through the rampaging lavender bushes, down towards the fatal corner. Maud followed, looking pained.

'*Children* — I said what are you doing down there among your grandfather's statues?'

'Just mucking about,' replied Betty coolly, wiping the dust from Apollo's serene forehead.

Beryl, Elsa and 'Ilda grinned impudently and sauntered away to a safe distance.

Diana put out her tongue at them.

'Mucking about! Mucking about ' giggled Sarah, pirouetting on her toes.

'Mucking about! Fucking about!' Deborah was at the age when rhymes delighted her.

'Children — *children* —' Maud and Clara swooped and screamed and drove their young ones back into the uncommon house, back into the drawing-room with its Bechstein, its rare, intricate chest from Germany, its wooden model of a village from Russia (that the children were allowed to play with on special occasions), its graceful portrait bust of Granny as a young woman.

'Next time I catch you talking to those common girls I shall punish you severely,' reprimanded Clara.

'We're going to have a BetDeb stall,' announced Betty gaily, never worried by her mother's threats. 'At Sarah's birthday bazaar.'

'Isn't Sawah a sweet, unselfish girl? To sacwifice her birthday party for poor Lily?' Maud caught sight of her own reflection in the glass covering one of her husband's paintings and she almost purred with satisfaction.

'Maud, you worry me!' pounced her matter-of-fact sister, still ruffled by Deborah's choice of words. 'You'll lose every scrap of sense one of these days. Preening and purring like a — like a —'

'Did someone call *children*?' Vicky, white from too much reading in a dark corner of Granny's bedroom, slid into the room. 'I thought I heard —'

'You're to do books,' said Diana. 'And pictures. We'd better go home now, or Mummy'll be cross. I'll explain as we go. Come on!'

The birthday dawned blue and golden; not a cloud disturbed the sky's transparency all the day.

The stalls were put up in the morning and their wares closely covered with cloths to await the business of the afternoon. The children had cooked, sewed, contrived, and written up to the *Ladies Home Journal* for all sorts of free samples. Vicky, rather frightened of

70

her elder sister who often teased and disapproved, dared not fail in her task and she ransacked every bookshelf at home, tore illustrations from her father's art books and stuck them on cardboard to sell as authentic pictures: when her thefts were discovered she was confined to her room one whole day on bread and water. The mothers all contributed loyally and Granny made pounds of fudge and a lot of rather ugly posies of raffia flowers.

The children all asked Mollie, nicely, if she could spare something.

Mollie was at a crisis in her life. She was red round the eyes as a result of many sleepless nights of tormenting suspicion and uncertainty. However, she said, 'Yes, of course, me darlin's. I'll turn out all the drawers and find you something really lovely.' When she forgot and they asked her again, she said. 'Don't you worry, sweethearts. I'll buy something brand new for you.'

Her sisters-in-law gave knowing smiles and said: 'Oh no, not Mollie! Not likely! She can't bear giving presents. She and John at least have *that* in common.'

When Mollie kept her word and presented each stall with a fine linen tray-cloth the sisters-in-law, implacably prejudiced, remarked: 'She'll get them back somehow. Without paying for them! She and Johnnie! Do you remember that time Johnnie brought us home "presents" from Moscow! Wasn't it shocking! Just like him, though! So mean!'

Everybody was invited, friends as well as relations.

Granny put on her best dress of blue silk with an immaculate lace collar. She esconced herself near the purple irises, sitting erect in a deck-chair, crocheting and beaming. Her antique sisters were there too — apparently unchanged since Christmas — Kennedy drowning in her white shawl although it was considered hot even for June, Tabby in her best black, Dooley in those white canvas shoes that turned up oddly at the toes, like a jester's hose, Sophia nibbling at something infinitesimal, continually working her jaws like a fastidious rabbit.

Everyone went first to the birthday Queen's stall with their presents and their purses. Her wares were original and clever and her stall was soon nearly empty. The others waited for their turn to be noticed. Diana, who was looking rather wan, hoped people would soon feel hungry.

Mollie, who would have preferred not to be there at all, moved over to talk to her.

'How's me pretty darlin' today?'

'Would you like a gingerbread man?' Diana deflected the question.

'I don't see Vickers here. Where is she?'

'Mummy wouldn't let her come.'

'Why?'

'Mummy was still cross about the book stall.'

'Where's your lively little brother. Where's dear little Ralph?'

'He's not well. Indigestion, or something.'

'Won't your mother be coming then?' She had counted on Dorothy as an ally. These family gatherings of women were always rather an ordeal for her. The company of the men did, at least sometimes, prevent some of the cattiness.

Today, of all days, she did not want to be alone among her critics. She and Johnnie had reached breaking-point. She was half-demented with worry and did not feel she could rely on her self-control; she was afraid she might do something unpredictable and terrible. She wanted Dorothy by her side, needed that astringent pride, that passionate scorn. Dorothy understood how impossible it had become to live in a corner of Granny's house, to be criticized all day long, to be spied on, condemned, edged out into the cold — a little more each day. Dorothy knew how much she longed for a house of her own: Dorothy probably guessed how much she regretted being childless, guessed the sense of failure this added to her other difficulties.

And Dorothy knew, also, something about the other side of Granny — the Granny who did *not* beam like a jolly goddess, did *not* heap up plates with food and fires with coal — the woman whom struggle, deprivation, ambition had made grasping, jealous, complaining.

'Will your mother be coming?' she repeated.

'I don't know,' replied Diana crossly, biting at her nails. 'She said she might.'

Actually her mother had been difficult about the party this afternoon, said it was an unnecessary fuss, said she was bored with the Seabridges and their occasions. Worst of all her new dress wasn't finished and her mother said, '*No*, we can't afford to go out and buy one ready-made. Certainly not. You'll have to wear your second-best, it isn't too tight for you, can't you see how busy and tired I am —' To Diana, who loved clothes as she did life, who cared for her appearance devotedly, this was almost intolerable. She, too, had wept last night.

'And how's me darlin' Diana?' Mollie pulled her thoughts round to the immediate present.

'You asked me that before.'

Mollie found a sort of ease by her niece's side. The pretty child had been ill, on and off, all that year, complaining of obscure pains, faintness and headaches. Dorothy had taken her to a number of doctors, but not one could really diagnose anything. Mollie felt protective and kind; these virtues bolstered up her wobbly self-esteem.

Diana made frantic signals to her cousins at the Bet-Deb stall. They were shortsighted and did not see. Maud did, however, and swayed to the rescue, perfuming the air around her with expensive scent.

Diana sighed with relief: she admired her Aunt Maud very much.

'Gingerbread men, Aunt Maud? Shortbread? It's made with real butter. Lemon curd tarts? The lemon curd's home-made.'

Maud filled her plate and offered coins. 'Aren't you eating, Mollie?'

Mollie had no appetite today, but she took the hint.

Diana smiled: a sixpence and six pennies now covered the bottom of her bowl.

'You always smell so lovely, Aunt Maud!'

Maud laughed, showing glistening teeth. 'Do I, dear? By the way, Mollie, Johnnie dwopped in to see us last night.'

'Oh?' murmured Mollie, clenching her fists.

'So he's going off again tomorrow?' Maud flashed another sweet smile.

Mollie stared hard at the pointed toes of her neat, black shoes and didn't answer.

'To Hungary this time, he said. Passing through Vienna on the way. Are you going with him?'

Mollie muttered something inaudible and hunched her shoulders.

'I wish Reggie went abroad more. And took little me with him. I feel so frustrated sometimes, shut up in my Chelsea flat.' She yawned elegantly and bit off a gingerbread leg. 'Or are you going to Budapest later? To bring him home?'

Mollie went very white, shouted, 'The truth is — oh,

leave me alone, can't you, you devil!' and quickly crossed the garden to the BetDeb stall.

The truth was that Johnnie was most certainly going to Hungary without her, that he was probably going in the fascinating company of the slim Annabella, that he might never come back, that she, Mollie, was wild with grief and didn't know what to do to save a lost situation.

Maud raised her beautiful eyebrows, said 'Aren't some people tiresome!' and bought three of Diana's rock cakes.

Mollie had her purse wide open to buy BetDeb wares. But the sight of the two girls at the stall froze her.

'Your dresses!' she gasped.

'What would you like, Auntie Mollie?' asked Betty, very politely. She preferred not to discuss the clothes she and Deborah were wearing. They were horrible dresses, *artistic* dresses.

'Your dresses!' repeated Mollie, sensing the girl's discomfiture, but unable to restrain herself.

She was fond of Betty and Deborah. Clara, she had to admit, was bringing them up well. They were thoughtful, truthful, obedient girls and she did not want to hurt their feelings. But — this was blasphemous — there must be *some* limit to art —

'Perhaps a toast rack?' Betty pretended not to hear. 'Daddy made it. Out of knitting-needles. You wouldn't guess, would you? Only sixpence.'

'You artists! Is there nothing holy? Nothing you'll leave alone, as it is?' Mollie couldn't help herself. 'Knitting-needles! Tablecloths!'

'What's the matter this time?' Clara came sharply to the rescue of her daughters.

'Their dresses are made out of a Russian tablecloth. I helped Johnnie choose it for you. Don't you remember?'

Mollie had two passions. One was Johnnie: the other was linen, which she hoarded and adored and could not resist buying. She had several lavender-scented drawers full of various cloths, napkins, handkerchiefs, loved counting them, spreading them out, refolding them. When grief or rage assailed her she could often calm herself by looking at her treasures, laying them against her hot forehead. She knew exactly where each one came from and the time of its purchase.

'Yes,' she insisted. 'He bought it in St. Petersburg. That winter when we went to a party on the frozen Neva. The winter Pavlova was at her best. He gave it to you for a present.'

'Present?' said Clara, and she laughed an acid laugh.

'Auntie Joyce, you'd like a toast rack, wouldn't you? Or how about this knitted rabbit for baby Jocelyn?' Betty raised her voice to drown the conversation. It was bad enough to have to wear such a monstrosity: to hear it being discussed, even in the snug bosom of the family, was insufferable.

Mollie was correct in her accusation. The dresses were both made from an enormous, heavy, Russian tablecloth. Betty and Deborah had, like Diana, longed for new summer party dresses — for ordinary party dresses, frilled, flounced and beribboned, if possible, like other children wore. But no — their mother had once more insisted on something original. She had counted the pence in her purse, had consulted her ingenious Salisbury, and with scissors and nimble fingers had busied herself with the linen cloth woven in Tsarist Russia from flax grown in the Ukraine. The results were interesting and rather strange. The material fell straight and cold and heavy; blue bands of embroidered birds relieved the austerity at neck, waist and sleeves. The girls looked half-way between

76

nuns and serfs. Granny and the others were ecstatic. Clever Clara!

'I think you've spoilt it, Clara dear,' announced Mollie in her most forthright voice. 'I remember seeing just such a cloth in a nobleman's house in St. Petersburg. Spread with champagne and caviar and lovely glasses that rang like bells when you touched them. The chandeliers were sparkling and the gipsies were playing their fiddles and the snow —' her voice became dreamy: that glamorous past was an antidote to present hell.

'Yes,' said Joyce. 'I'll have the little knitted rabbit, darling.'

'And Johnnie brought you all home expensive gifts!' Mollie returned briskly to the present. 'Something for each of you. I chose them.'

'And after he'd given them to us,' narrated Clara tartly, 'and we'd all thanked him — we'd never had such lovely presents before — he roared with laughter and said, "Now then, girls, pay up!" And he made us pay for them. Presents! Not Johnnie!'

'What are you saying about my Johnnie boy?' called out Granny from her deck-chair.

'Just saying how vewy good to you he is, Mother,' called back Maud. 'Giving you such a lovely house to live in.'

'Are you joining him in Budapest, Mollie?' asked Joyce, meaning to be kind. She had been so busy with her babies that current gossip had hardly reached her.

'What's wrong with the lot of you?' whispered Mollie. 'Have you no pity, any of you?'

'Everything on my stall's sold!' A radiant Sarah burst into the locked group. 'Now we can have fun. Let's have tea. And then count the money.'

Her word was law this afternoon. The children

escaped from their stalls and dashed for the strawberries and cream. The juice squelched between their lips. It splashed down on to Deborah's vestal robes, staining them as though with blood. Betty followed her young sister's innocent example, making certain she would never be garbed in a tablecloth again. Happily eating, they all wandered about the garden, glad to be free of doing good to Lily Longton.

'Let's play some games now,' suggested Granny, who was managing to eat an enormous bowl of strawberries and continue with her crocheting at the same time. 'How about *I sent a letter to my love*?'

'We're a bit too old for that, Granny,' laughed Sarah.

'Let's have a little sing-song and a dance then. Clara, you go in and play the piano and open the window. Play loudly.'

'Have you all gone deaf?' Dorothy suddenly appeared in the middle of a polka. 'I've been standing at the front door knocking and knocking. Vicky had to climb in through the window and let me in.'

'Dorothy darlin', I'm so glad to see you.' Mollie blew her nose emotionally on an exquisite lace handkerchief. 'And Vickers. And Ralph — are you better, sweetheart?'

Ralph slid out of her embrace like water and hurried to the end of the garden, from where he could just see the trains crossing a distant bridge. Vicky helped herself to the last of the strawberries.

'You're late, Dorothy, you're late,' reprimanded Granny. 'You shouldn't be late on Sarah's birthday.'

'We've made two pounds seven shillings and sevenpence,' shouted Sarah. 'It's marvellous. Thank you, everyone, for being so nice and helpful. We'll have to plan a special presentation ceremony when we give it all to Lily.'

'Oh no we won't!' said Betty resolutely. She had grown up a lot this afternoon. She had made up her mind that never again would she submit either to Sarah's bossiness or to the shame of artistic clothes. In future she would design her own clothes.

'If we can't have games we'll have photographs,' decided Granny. 'It's time we had some more taken. Joyce, a nice group of the children. You brought the camera, didn't you?'

'Yes, Mother. It's in the bedroom. Who'll run and get it for me? Diana?'

'We haven't got time to stay for photographs,' said Dorothy.

'But you've only just come,' lamented Granny.

'Everything all right, dear?' asked Joyce quietly. The only one of the sisters who had yet experienced real grief herself she was perceptive where others were concerned and she was a woman of genuine and lavish kindness. She knew that things were often very strained between Dorothy and Bernard, that devotion to his sculpture often transported Bernard into a kingdom not of this world where no one could follow him, not even his own true love: she knew that money worries sometimes fretted Dorothy till her nerve shook. She did not completely understand this complex sister-in-law of hers — who did? — but she loved her.

'Bernard hasn't spoken to me for ten days,' replied Dorothy. 'Not one single word. I don't know why.'

'He's probably wrestling with his art, dear.'

'And I'm so worried about Diana. She's still not very well, you know.'

'She's looking so lovely today, dear. I always think she's the prettiest of the girls — that lovely pink-and-gold colouring, and that sweet, serious little expression.'

79

'Children — gather round me —' came Granny's voice. 'The syringa'll make a graceful background. Got the camera, Joyce?'

'Here's Diana with it now. Come along, children. All of you — Vicky, come down from that tree — Ralph — You take Jocelyn on your lap, Mother.'

'Thank God you came, Dorothy,' Mollie said as the children grimaced and the camera clicked. 'They've been pulling me down this afternoon.'

'Oh, Mollie, I'm so sorry. And I've got so many worries on my mind, too. Let's go for a long walk to-morrow and have a talk. Over Wimbledon Common and through Richmond Park.' Dorothy was a valiant walker. The exercise calmed her. She enjoyed pitting her will-power against her physical fatigue and going on and on.

'Tomorrow? Oh, Dorothy darlin', haven't you heard?'

'Heard what?' Dorothy was strangely innocent in some ways.

'Johnnie and — and — that — oh, Dorothy, it's killin' me.'

'Hasn't it been a gorgeous party?' Sarah lolled on the grassy bank. 'I love organizing bazaars. When I'm grown up I shall devote myself to charity and good works and telling people what to do.'

'I shall devote myself to my family,' said Betty. 'That's a woman's first duty. I'm going to have lots of children. What about you, Diana?'

'I want to be rich and be able to buy all the clothes I want. I want to marry someone I adore and never have any quarrels.'

'I think I'll be some sort of an artist,' said Deborah, loyal to the family tradition.

'And I'm going round the world,' called Vicky, high in the air on the swing. 'I'm going to take a team of huskies to Alaska. I want to stand on the top of Everest and shout.'

'I wonder,' mused Diana. 'What will happen to us. Do you think our wishes'll come true?'

'Of *course* they will,' promised Sarah.

Some were to blossom and some to fall by the wayside. One of the grandchildren was to grow important in the eyes of the world, another would be very clever, another go only from sorrow to sorrow. One would be an outsider, another a recluse, another the epitome of convention. It was probably just as well they could not see ahead.

'STRAWBERRIES!' roared a familiar voice. 'Hope you've saved some for ME!'

'Johnnie!' exclaimed Granny and Mollie together.

John came lightly down the steps into the garden, tossed a package to Sarah and headed for the tea table.

What happened next was swift and shocking.

Mollie suddenly by his side, clutched his lapels and said, 'I'm not going to let you go.' Johnnie laughed and gave her a shove that broke her hold and almost toppled her over. Mollie recovered, sprang at him and clawed his spectacles from his face, scratching him as she did so. John yelled and lunged out at her: without his glasses he was half blind. Mollie waved them in the air, crying 'I'm going to hide them. I won't let you leave me,' and she went into the house. John lumbered after her. Joyce and Clara followed. Maud put her arms round Sarah and told her not to look. Granny turned white and bit on her crochet hook. Kennedy hid her face in her shawl and Tabby scratched her head wildly. Dorothy gathered her family together and said they must go home at once.

A sound of shouting came out of the open door and the children pressed up to see more. A window opened in the common house next door and a head popped out to look. Granny groaned and also went indoors, moving as quickly as a girl and shutting the back door firmly against the children. Dorothy repeated 'Come along children. Say good-bye to everyone.'

There was only Maud, who believed in leaving her sisters to cope with awkward situations, to say good-bye to. Diana dutifully kissed her and said to her mother, 'Aunt Maud always smells heavenly. Why don't you?'

Dorothy said, 'A woman is never so good as when she smells of nothing. So said Aristotle.'

And Deborah, who still could not resist rhymes, added 'Aristotle — hot water bottle —'

Betty and Sarah pressed up against the windows and tried to see how the drama was developing. 'Whatever's happening?' they wondered. 'What on earth can the matter be?'

It would be a long time before they knew the inside story.

At the next bazaar Sarah organized they made over fifty pounds which they presented to the Sunshine Homes for Blind Babies. But that was several years away and many things, happy and sad, happened in between.

CHAPTER FIVE

ONE Saturday morning when white clouds towered high in the sky Bernard said to his daughter Vicky: 'I'm coming with you to the "Green Man" this morning.'

'You? With me?'

It was rare for Bernard to go anywhere with his children. He preferred to shake them off the moment he stepped outside the house: should he chance to meet them in the street he would bow with impeccable courtesy and pass on his way. Unlike his brother-in-law, Salisbury, who adored children and only forebade his daughters and their friends the freedom of the studio when he had a naked model, Bernard chose to be alone with his blocks of stone and bins of clay, his tools and his visions.

'Yes, my dear, Mr. Nathan's expecting me.' Bernard stretched his right hand out in front of him, bent and unbent the supple fingers, pivoted his forearm backwards and forwards. With a small frown of concentration he studied the ripple of muscles under the skin. 'He knows I'm coming. Now, run along and get ready.'

Perplexed and excited, Vicky did as she was told.

What on earth could her father want at the 'Green Man' — at Mr. Nathan's odorous, fascinating stables? It was extraordinary.

But the atmosphere at home, at Gateway Cottage up the hill from Granny's, had been rather extraordinary this last week or two. The furniture was all topsy-turvy. Her father wandered from room to room frowning and in the evenings would sit at the piano and rage through the finale of the Appassionata. Her mother burst into snatches of tuneless song, murmured to herself and was altogether rather absent-minded, forgetting to put rice in the pudding, for instance, so that a dish of sloppy baked milk would be served up, to everyone's amusement. She was, however, indulging in an orgy of jam-making, pounds and pounds of it; never had there been such a bubbling and seething of hot, squelchy fruit in the kitchen, such a fragrance in the air. Carefully labelled jars glowing with their rich contents stood about everywhere. Jam was, of course, made every summer — this was part of the domestic ritual of those days when fruit could still be bought very cheaply — but never before in such gargantuan quantities.

Yes, there was a crackle of highly-charged anticipation in the air. Something momentous was obviously about to happen. But Vicky had no idea what. And Diana, who might have explained things, had gone away somewhere.

'Your father told you he's going with you, did he?' Dorothy put the usual carrots for the horses into a paper bag. 'He'll be taking you on to your granny's afterwards. You're going to stay with her two or three days.'

'Ralph? Is he too?'

'No, you're going by yourself this time, darling. I've put your nightie and slippers and things in this

84

basket. Remember to do all you can to help Granny. Clean your teeth night and morning. And remember your Auntie Mollie is a good woman. You're not to believe anything your Granny says about her. And brush your hair every night. Now, run along darling. I'm awfully busy. And your father doesn't like to be kept waiting.'

She tilted back her head, looking through the kitchen window up at those billowing clouds. 'How I *wish* I could come with you!' The sudden expression of rapture on her face made her look like a dreamy, beautiful girl. 'I'm tired of being indoors. Oh, I *am* so tired. I'd love to go for a long walk today, over the Common with the wind in my face. All the ling'll be in full flower.' With a sigh she pulled herself together. 'Never mind. I'm glad you'll be out in the open air, darling. Off you go. I've got such a lot to do. Oh dear, ever such a lot.'

The family was moving house. But how was Vicky to know? Explanations were not usually given to children in those days. It was not then the fashion to burden them with the responsibility of free choice, include them in family discussions, consider their callow reasons overmuch. For better or for worse children lived in a world apart, a world of mystery and conjecture—lonely, magical, terrifying, thrilling, astonishing.

So, without knowing what or why, Vicky left Gateway Cottage and set off with that stranger, her father, for her fortnightly riding lesson on one of Mr. Nathan's hard-mouthed hacks. She was never to return to that home.

This departure took place on a breezy summer morning not very long after Sarah's birthday, when Maud had smelt of heaven and Dorothy had smelt of nothing and Mollie had gone mad.

Dorothy and Mollie had not yet managed to have their walk together, that exorcizing tramp over Wimbledon Common and through Richmond Park.

The mauve acres of ling would have faded to brown, the silver birches have shaken off their last golden leaves, the ice be closing in round the shy haunts of the water-birds on Pen Ponds and the north wind be hissing in a purple sky before the two friends found time to be together again. Life was embroiling them too deeply at present for them to be able to put on their sensible walking-shoes, cut their wholemeal bread-and-cheese sandwiches and stride out to disemburden their hearts.

Mollie's life had grown so chaotic that she was only capable of living from hour to hour. She surfaced each time the postman dropped letters through the box, then sank back into alternating moods of frenzy and apathy. John had, needless to say, put on a spare pair of glasses and gone off to Budapest via Vienna, where his graceful Annabella had, no doubt, given him warm hospitality and solaced him with Viennese songs: he had not yet returned and she did not even know if he would return. In her anguish Mollie did not know what to do; Granny told her daughters she was even starting to sell the furniture for whisky.

And Dorothy's worries were thickening round her to such an extent that she found it impossible to stretch out a friendly hand and try and haul Mollie from the abyss.

Diana's intermittent periods of illness were becoming sharper and more frequent; specialists began to murmur terrifying possibilities. And then there was this move, this move she didn't really want and that now and again made her heart contract with a spasm of dread. She wanted to devote herself to getting Diana strong and well. She feared the tearing up of roots, all the fuss and disturbance; nor did she feel easy about the new house. She didn't think it was going to be the right sort of home for them. Several times, as zero hour approached, she woke in the night cold with apprehension.

She was happy at Gateway Cottage. It was warm and dry, free from mice and blackbeetles, had a small garden where the washing could blow dry, wide and windy Heaths where the children could run wild in safety. Her longed-for son had been born here, anchoring her with joy. It was just exactly right for an artist's home, too — quiet and tucked-away. True, there was a dearth of cupboard space, the kitchen was crowded if two people washed up together and Bernard had to cycle some miles every day to his studio. But it was a *happy* place. A beautiful magnolia grew against the south wall, a thrush came every year to nest in the honeysuckle over the arbour, the golden evening sun shone into all four little bedrooms, there was room for their maid, Rose, to live-in with them.

Home-loving, unacquisitive, self-denying, she would have been content to stay there all her life, helping the children grow up sturdy and straight, enjoying now and then the company of a few choice friends, studying (and sometimes writing) poetry, translating German stories, embroidering, reading aloud from the classics, sometimes hopping on a District Line train and going to the West End to applaud the acting of Gielgud or the piano playing of Cortot. It was Bernard who decided and insisted, who fought to get away from the prim life of the suburbs into what he hoped would be a freer environment where people all addressed each other by their christian names and did not pry into their neighbours' affairs from behind lace curtains. He was an important sculptor now; people predicted he

87

would go from strength to strength. Both abroad and in England many works from his hand had been erected in public places. It was he who had been chosen to execute the great Guards Memorial on the Horse Guards Parade. He was becoming fashionable: he needed a good address.

Dorothy had always found her deepest fulfilment in serving Bernard, in trying to smooth difficulties from his ambitious path and in helping him through creative crises. It was not for her to cross him in this move. Even so, she did gently query its wisdom.

'The new house is so small, darling. And there's absolutely nowhere for the children to play. Nowhere at all. Do you think —'

'But it's built now. And the front-door keys are cut. Do be reasonable, my dear.'

'I know it sounds silly, darling. It's just that I wake in the night sometimes and feel frightened. I feel we may have to sacrifice too much.'

'Nonsense. It is freehold, you know.'

'I didn't exactly mean that —'

'You're just feeling a bit overtired.'

'Yes, perhaps that's it.'

'You know yourself how you're looking forward to it really. You've been saying how nice it'll be to be near the theatres and exhibitions. And we'll be able to have splendid parties in the studio.'

'Yes, darling, perhaps you're right. I'm probably just being a stupid.'

Why should anyone take her foolish fancies seriously? After all, no one had paid any attention to poor, mad Cassandra when she cried, 'Woe, Woe,' before the fall of Troy.

'I hope', she said, with a characteristic change of mood, 'that the architect's left space for a bicycle shed.

We can't stack them in the hall if you're planning to entertain the Duke of Connaught and the Prince of Wales.'

To this wry sally Bernard could find no reply. He hadn't thought about a bicycle shed. But in tricky matrimonial debates his policy was to let the other person have the last word. Dorothy took advantage of his calculated silence and, deciding to make the best of the inevitable, declared: 'At least the kitchen's much larger. I shall have lots of space for store cupboards. I'm going to make pots and pots of jam to take with us.'

In a turmoil of boiling and stirring, bottling and labelling her apprehensions subsided.

Dorothy and Bernard had an unusual thing in common.

They were both children of a mother who had been suddenly widowed and left to bring up five children single-handed. Each was, therefore, accustomed to an absolutely matriarchal government. Neither could refer back to an ordinary sort of childhood and this lack of any father must have accounted for many of the difficulties they experienced in bringing up their own children.

Dorothy came from a Kentish family, all of them good-looking in a fair, fine-boned way. They had high foreheads and the delicately hollowed temples of lovers of beauty; the two girls had that sort of soft, fine complexion that the years wear away to the texture of old ivory. All had strong, blue eyes and, dedicated pantheists, could never look too long or too deeply at the world of nature. They were the sort of people who knew where, and when, to go and hear nightingales singing, who could recognize a hawk high up where most other people saw only haze, knew the banks where the best wild strawberries grew, were familiar with the planets and constellations. Somewhere back along the line they had Florence Nightingale and other ardent reformers, and it was said that further back still they could lay claim to that profligate old Duke, John of Gaunt: but they all had too much pride and self-esteem to care about ancestors long dead and buried.

They were a nervous, excitable, brave and energetic bunch, often unpredictable and inconsistent and with an odd streak of 'otherness' about them, a sort of wild mysticism. Now and again one or another of them saw ghosts, had prophetic dreams, heard inner voices or saw visions. Explorers of ideas, they tended to push their searches farther and farther, to the extreme fringes of possibility; sometimes they lost control of their dreams and intuitions, or they flew too high to keep in touch with the world. Few things are more perilous than a dream that runs amuck and there were things that could not be spoken of easily in that family history.

The Seabridges had had their three successive generations of widows and the gentle Joyce, trying to superimpose order on the chaos of grief, had suggested a curse. A generation later one of Dorothy's children, faced with an appalling sequence of events and co-incidences, was to wonder whether in their case, too, there had been a curse. Some cranky, twisted old grandsire could well have damned his successors in an irresponsible fit of rage, or lust, casting out three generations into the wilderness, pushing them to the cold edges of society.

These catastrophes and discoveries were, however, a long, long way off in the future. The present was comparatively serene.

When Dorothy wished, she could be one of the most

delightful, beguiling women anyone could choose to know. A natural listener, friends and strangers poured out their secrets to her; a witty, lively talker, her company was much sought. Elusive, idealistic, with the imagination of a poet and the curiosity of a scientist, her moods were infinitely varied. Irritating, puzzling, disturbing, eccentric she might be — but never boring. In the afternoon she could be down on her hands and knees scrubbing the floors like a sailor and then emerge in the evening, looking like one of Botticelli's Graces, to attend some reception, wearing perhaps a shimmering bronze-green dress with antique, gold ear-rings swinging against her long neck — a dazzling vision to her children when she kissed them good night. One moment she might be bouncing a ball with the glee of a girl and the next all hunched up and contorted with pain as she read some newspaper account of injustice. She genuinely enjoyed a spartan kind of life; luxury was abhorrent to her. Utterly truthful, she was incapable of understanding deception in others. Later in life she ventured to the outposts of political life: the tissue of intrigue, however, and the necessity for diplomatic lies went too much against the grain of her nature for her to enter fully into this bustling, ambitious milieu. She was the sort of person, almost extinct in the present era, who would choose to be burnt at the stake rather than live out a lie.

Her friends loved her for everything, her enemies denounced her inability to compromise, her fiercely puritanical beliefs. Her children adored her sense of fun, her ready sympathy, the stories she told them, and they feared her when she was angry and lashed out at them with intolerable sarcasm. Willy-nilly, Bernard was bound to her all his life: in every statue there she was — the tender nape of her neck, the high forehead and classical features. When age began to wither her beauty he could hardly bear it: he pinned up in his studio a photo of Rodin's figure 'La Vieille Heaulmière' as if to remind himself that he was not alone in his pain and that if the great Rodin could endure it so could he.

'You enjoy your riding lessons?' asked Bernard as he and Vicky set out together. He was a jaunty walker and she had to run to keep up with him. 'Have you a favourite horse?'

'Hm — no — not exactly.' She could not explain to him that Mr. Nathan's tired geldings were shadows compared to the imaginary horse she rode, Captain Flint, who was black as Egypt's night, who could jump as high as the lamp-posts and gallop like a racehorse. 'They're all nice really.'

'One day I hope you'll be able to go and see the greatest horse in the world. The horse outside the cathedral at Padua. By Donatello.'

'Oh — Donatello —'

'I first saw that statue in the pouring rain. It was glistening with water and it looked really grand silhouetted against the stormy sky.'

Bernard was not a man for the nursery world. He had no idea how to talk to children, being always too daemon-haunted to be granted entry to their small world. Some artists have a simplicity of mind that makes them feel more at ease with children than with their contemporaries. Bernard was not like this. Yet something in his unusual conversation kindled young imaginations and children often remembered his sayings.

'Yes, I always maintain it was worth while winning the Rome scholarship if only to see this great work. You know, it was Donatello who said *If you would be a sculptor you must draw, draw, draw.*'

'Did he? You know — I don't think I'll be a sculptor.'

'No, my dear, I shouldn't. It's a dreadfully hard life. Nothing but work, work. And in the winter I get awful chilblains from handling the cold, wet clay. Your mother came out to join me in Rome, you know. The Romans loved her, but she found their attentions rather tiresome. She's a very high-minded woman, your mother. They loved her fairness. And she was very pretty. Your sister Diana takes after her. You, my dear —' he glanced sardonically down at the child by his side, 'are said to resemble me. Poor you!'

'Oh.'

They turned left into Putney Hill and were momentarily silenced by the whizz of traffic.

Bernard was one of those men who grow better-looking as they age. Now, in his forties, he was undeniably plain and often looked haggard. He had to wrestle with many dark angels and the struggles sometimes reduced him to a shadow. Away from his family people said he was very amusing and often the life and soul of parties. He attracted all sorts of men and women, having that intuitive sympathy and quick response that is bound up with the creative personality, that functions independently of the will. Honourable, obstinate, fastidious, touchy, he was found to be — by people who had the staying power to penetrate his great shyness and modesty — very wise and very kind. Where his work was concerned he never spared himself anything in order to produce the best of which he was capable, not counting the cost in time, money or agony.

'So you enjoy your riding lessons? I'm glad. When your mother suggested you learning I must confess I thought it an unnecessary extravagance. But she

93

insisted. She said it would give you confidence. She's a very determined woman, your mother.'

'Is she?'

'It's riding the bicycle she loves. Do you know — well, I'll tell you something. It upset me very much at the time. Before you were born, during the war, I was in camp, in Sussex, waiting to be shipped abroad. And your mother came down from London to see me. All the way from London on a bicycle. And she rode straight into the camp on her bicycle. And do you know — round her neck she was wearing a feather boa. Just imagine! On a bicycle, with a long *feather boa* hanging round her neck. It looked very odd. Everyone saw. It upset me very much. I couldn't bring myself to speak to her. Nor could I tell her why I couldn't bring myself to speak to her.'

'Golly!' Vicky made a mental to look up *feather boa* in the *Encyclopaedia* when she got to Granny's: it sounded weird.

'Yes, we had rather a silent week-end.' Bernard's deep voice was muffled as though the memory still offended him. 'Your mother didn't understand why. And I simply couldn't tell her.'

They were half-way up the Hill now: breezes skidded off the Common and refreshed them.

'Mr. Nathan has kindly agreed to lend me his best horse', explained Bernard gently.

'The chestnut?'

'Is that the best one?'

'He's very spirited. He bucks. You'll have a job to stay on.' Vicky looked anxiously up at him. Oh dear — would he borrow some boots, like she did? Would he keep on that large, faded brown hat of his? And what about his pince-nez — wouldn't they fall off at the first trot? Everyone would look at him and she would then feel ashamed and wish herself invisible. How awful!

'I'm not going to *ride* him. I just want to *draw* him.'

'Oh —' She sighed with relief.

'Yes, I've been invited to take part in another competition. I have to submit a sketch model for a statue to be erected in Whitehall — a statue of Earl Haig — on horseback. It's a challenging subject. Don't you think so?'

'Most! Oh yes, most!'

They had come to the top of the Hill at last, and there, in front of them, lay the promised stables. With joy Vicky rushed towards the strong, sweet smell of hay and leather, escaping from her father's incomprehensible, memorable words. She vanished into a small, inner sanctum, there to undergo the painful ceremony called 'putting on the riding boots'. Dorothy had said yes, all right, she could learn riding, but no, she would have to manage without the expense of breeches and things. So she managed in her ordinary, Saturday-morning clothes — and Mr. Nathan kindly helped out with the loan of some antiquated, wrinkled, knee-length boots. To enable these to go on, yellow stable soap had first of all to be rubbed copiously over her feet to make them slippery and then one or two people had to pull very hard.

While this ritual was being performed Mr. Nathan led Bernard into the stables where the mettlesome chestnut was firmly secured. Bernard walked all round the animal, studying him intently, and then seated himself on an upturned box, sharpened his Venus pencils and delved for his sketch book. The horse turned his lovely head and looked full at Bernard with melancholy, disdainful eyes.

'What a neck!' exclaimed Bernard.

'Up you go!' said Mr. Nathan, giving Vicky a hoist. 'Stirrups all right? You'd better have the right one up a couple of holes. Bob —' he shouted to a young man wearing purple riding boots, 'come and see to your pupil.'

'Look at it! That neck!' repeated Bernard. 'What an arch! Those muscles — that trapezius, that mastoidus! That's just exactly how I want him.'

'Gee up!' said Vicky to her unwilling mount.

'In my mind,' said Bernard, 'I'd planned a monumental statue of Haig. You know — high up on an enormous pedestal, like a saviour above his people. But the horse's neck is telling me differently, is reminding me of the dogged character of the General, that tough soldier who said *With our backs to the wall and believing in the justice of our cause* — and so on. I must emphasize that grim resolve of his to take on the whole German Army if he had to. I shall repeat the curve of the horse's neck in the intent curve of Haig's body —'

'The jolly old spirit moves, in fact,' said the affable Mr. Nathan, feeling this might be the right sort of thing to say.

'Good-bye!' called Vicky. 'We're going.'

But Bernard, caught up in these fresh flights of inspiration, did not reply. As her horse clattered across the cobbled yard she heard him say. 'In sculpting any figure, man or horse, we have to start at the beginning. Bones, muscle, flesh, skin. This horse now — we must get down to the bones —'

Half-fearing some gruesome scene of skinning alive if she looked back, Vicky rode straight on by the side of the young man with the purple boots. The wind on the Heath slapped vigour into the apathetic hacks; they breathed in summer earth and bracken, whinnied and started forward.

'Steady! 'Old 'im!' shouted the young man as Vicky's horse broke into a canter.

'I'll try —'

She was not a natural horsewoman. These riding lessons were little more than a long struggle to control an iron-mouthed horse with an inclination to bolt, interspersed with instructions to 'Rein 'im back! Slow 'im down! Well then, grab 'old of 'is bloody ear, gal!'

Her skirt blew up into her face, her hair rose straight up on end, the earth thudded by below her, the wind roared above. She was the Grand National winner, she was the Charge of the Light Brigade. Later she always paid for these raptures with blisters and aches. But the joy of the game was well worth it.

Granny said she smelt of horses and gave her a bath. She was sent into the garden to pick sprigs of rosemary which were then simmered in water to soften it for hair-washing. Leaving her with egg yolk all over her scalp and her head bent over a basin, Granny dashed out to the greengrocer to buy lemons for a rinse. Vicky emerged from these ablutions feeling damp and downy as a newly-hatched chick.

Tossing and turning that night on the uncomfy bed (Granny loved having people sleeping in her bedroom and had put up a camp bed for her), she was woken several times by the rumbling of the trains and by Granny's cheerful snoring. When she did fall soundly asleep she dreamed that her mother was riding round the room on a bicycle with a winged boa-constrictor coiled like a lasso about her shoulders.

It had been difficult getting to the Encyclopaedias unobserved. Not that they were forbidden books, but she was never quite sure if she ought to, as they were so often connected with words the grown-ups wouldn't tell you the meaning of. Normally, with aunts and cousins all over the place, she was able to go about her business unnoticed: accustomed to the uproar of parties she found the house uncannily quiet now. Getting along the passage into the drawing-room where the Encyclopaedias lived was rather like a macabre game of Grandmother's Footsteps. At a creak from a floorboard Granny's face would jump round the kitchen door — not her benevolent Christmas face, but a countenance pale and stretched with suspicion, her big nose jutting out like a question mark. 'Oh, it's *you*, is is, love? Bless you!' she would say as Vicky froze guiltily and retreated to base to try again.

The house was almost unrecognizable; it groaned and shuddered with an invisible ballast of woe. Occasionally Mollie slid along the passage like a red-faced ghost and once or twice Vicky thought she heard her shouting at Granny.

It can never have occurred to Granny as she wished and hoped for Mollie's downfall that she herself might be involved in the shipwreck. Events have a way of growing beyond the people who will them and of trapping the actors in their own ill-considered calculations. Certainly Granny can never have envisaged being left to hold the baby, to live alone with her abandoned daughter-in-law. The situation was becoming intolerable. Granny didn't think she could bear it much longer and was beginning to wonder if she could find a flat for herself somewhere down on the South Coast, near where Clara and Salisbury had built their seaside cottage. In her practical way she even made enquiries at agents in Worthing, although in her heart she raged at being driven to this. The injustice was unbelievable. It should not be she planning to leave the pretty Oxford Road house: it should be Mollie, the unwanted, the deserted. Had the woman no pride, no dignity?

Vicky came face to face with Mollie on Sunday evening on the threshold of the bathroom and was horrified to find herself enfolded in a bear's hug. 'Oh, Vickers, Vickers — I wish I had a little girl like you. Your mother and I were married on the same day, at the same Registry Office. And do you know, me lovely darlin' — the Clerk made a mistake and I was nearly married to your Father instead. It might have been better if I had been. Oh yes, it might have been better —'

Granny's house was, indeed, in limbo: Vicky was thankful to hear that Sarah would be coming for the afternoon the next day.

Sarah brought authority and balance with her. She also brought a fruit cake, an apple tart, butter and half a pound of ham. Granny had been so upset by events that her famous appetite threatened to desert her: her daughters were very worried and took every opportunity to send her baskets of food. When Sarah came into the kitchen wearing a pretty pink dress she had made herself, tension relaxed and things started to be funny again. And when they sat down to tea Granny's normal zest began to return and her craving for perfection to reassert itself.

'Beetroot!' she announced. 'I just fancy some beetroot with this ham!' She looked at her grandchildren, who both looked out of the window, wondering if beetroot grew in the garden. 'Well, if you won't do anything about it, I suppose I shall have to go to the greengrocer myself,' she said rather crossly, and she immediately rose from the table, put on her hat and coat and left the house.

'Oh dear,' said Sarah guiltily. 'I suppose I should have offered to go for her.'

Ten minutes later Granny was back with a large, steaming beetroot. She ate it all with relish and it put her in such a good humour that after tea she sat down at the piano and for an hour played English folk songs for the children to sing.

When Bernard came to fetch Vicky he had a message to deliver to Granny. He did not want to deliver it; he really wanted no part in this matter that seemed to him sordid and humiliating. But he had promised Salisbury he would tell Granny, as he was going to see her, and Bernard was never a man to go back on his word, or to sidle away from an unpleasant task.

'Johnnie's back in England,' he said, making sure the children were out of the way. 'He's brought Annabella with him.'

'Johnnie — *back* —' she half rose from the sofa, blushing like a girl. 'And now I shall be able to meet Annabella and make her welcome. For Johnnie's sake.'

Had Bernard not been standing with his back to her looking glumly out of the window he would have seen that she was suddenly twenty years younger.

'John's found a flat near Tottenham Court Road,' he continued flatly,' and he and Annabella will live there until the divorce. John's also found a flat in Chelsea where he thinks Mollie should be comfortable. He'll be able to give her enough to live happily on. He's been promoted to an important position in his firm.'

He turned round and sat down: his duty was accomplished.

'And me?' Fear and jealousy clutched at Granny's heart. 'What about me? *My* allowance. Will he be able to afford all of us?'

Bernard covered his face with his left hand. There were times when his mother appalled him. He hardly liked to admit this to himself, but it was one of the reasons why he was so determined to live in another part of London.

'Don't worry, Mother,' he said, after a little struggle with himself. 'You'll never want for anything. I promise you.'

The affair shocked him. He hated having anything to do with it. He had meant to go on and tell Granny that Salisbury was feeling very pleased because he'd just won a prize of money in a *News-Chronicle* 'Ad-Cut' competition, but he was momentarily too upset to find the words.

'How's the Haig going, love?' Granny sensed his cold disapproval and rushed to make amends. 'I do hope you'll get the job. I'm sure you deserve to.'

Bernard's respect was necessary to her: she hated there to be dissent among the family. She loved Bernard for his many gifts and merits, for that comical sense of humour that could sometimes set her rocking. His supple, creative hands were so similar in shape and activity to his father's that she sometimes wondered if she were seeing things. He was absolutely steady and reliable. But it was John, clever, naughty Johnnie with all his tricks and deceptions, who illuminated life for her, who made her glow. It was not simply that Johnnie could do no wrong: in her eyes Johnnie was a law unto himself. He was a natural thruster, strong as a high tide; he was a bounder who could leap too far and too swiftly ever to be caught and pinned down. If his methods were sometimes rough, well, this might be because the great energy in him surged and sparkled. It was as though the electricity that dominated his working life charged him with more force than the ordinary run of people.

'My work — oh yes —' Bernard shrugged his

shoulders expressively, kissed Granny's cheek and took his daughter away from the suburbs to her new home in the fashionable congestion of Kensington, away from the friendly cottage and the carefree escapades on the Common to the constriction of a town house and dull walks in Kensington Gardens.

The two large studios, with new house attached, stood in a picturesque cul-de-sac; nearly all the neighbours were engaged in some artistic profession — it was quite a little colony. The studios were magnificent; the house was, if anything, even smaller, quainter and more tucked-away than Gateway Cottage had been. Dorothy, who liked gardening, had not a blade of grass to call her own. Worse still, the architect, cutting down Bernard's expenses wherever he could, had economized on cupboards and larders. The kitchen did not even boast a shelf. Dorothy was white with disappointment; there was nowhere to put a tea caddy, let alone the hundred and fifty pounds of jam. At length Bernard said, rather grudgingly, 'All right, my dear, they can go in the studio for the time being. In the back studio. Behind the bins of clay.'

In the first few weeks two ceilings fell down — one on Ralph's bed, the other in the middle of the dining-room table. Luckily no one was hurt, but it was rather a nuisance and that old sense of foreboding returned to worry Dorothy. She bravely pushed it away from her but, nevertheless, a certain uneasiness remained.

To many people's surprise (Bernard almost invariably won the competitions for which he entered) the Haig commission was awarded to Mr. Alfred Hardiman. Controversy raged in the newspapers. The general opinion was that Bernard's resolute, stern General reining in his horse was more imaginative and more truthful than Hardiman's conventional, pompous hero.

Bernard took his disappointment manfully and looked around for other work. He did remark, however, that the pedestal of Hardiman's statue ('A very fine pedestal, mark you!') was obviously much inspired by Donatello's pedestal at Padua.

'And that statue,' he repeated, 'was the first equestrian statue to be erected for a thousand years after the fall of Rome. I shouldn't be surprised,' he added prophetically, 'if this statue of Haig doesn't turn out to be the last equestrian statue to be erected for another thousand years. The day of the horse is done for the time being!'

CHAPTER SIX

Clara went into her husband's studio calling out, 'Salisbury, Miss Smith's sent her maid round for her breasts. She wants to see if they fit.'

'Oh yes! The paint's just dried. Wait a jiffy while I wrap 'em up.'

As he packed the actress's false bosom (a rubber ball cut in half, turned inside out and painted flesh colour) Clara looked around the studio and she sighed.

'I thought you were supposed to be finishing that relief for the cinema,' she said. 'It's nowhere near done.'

'Something rather urgent cropped up.'

'What?'

'Someone asked me to make a donkey for a children's party. You know, the sort with a tail you pin on blindfold.'

'Oh, Salisbury! And all those bills to pay!'

'Wait a tick and I'll show you. I'll just take these to the maid and explain how they go on. Then I'll show you the donkey. It'll make you laugh!'

'I don't feel like laughing. I haven't got time. You know I'm supposed to be packing. You haven't forgotten we're going down to Clymping first thing to-morrow, have you?'

But Salisbury had gone. And Clara waited, in spite of herself, partly because people always did wait for Salisbury and partly because the work he did for fun and for love was always worth seeing.

'Ah — you're still there. Here's the masterpiece —'

In its way it was a masterpiece, imagined on the spur of the moment, worked out with brilliant craft. It was not an ordinary, run-of-the-mill cardboard donkey but a wooden dragon, garishly-painted and with a fierce Chinese face, and instead of a dull old tail to be pinned on the rump he had made a sword to be plunged into the dragon's ferocious heart.

'And Clara, when the sword pierces the vital part — listen —'

He took the sword and stabbed: the dragon opened his hideous jaw and groaned.

'Won't the children enjoy it! How they'll laugh!'

'But Salisbury,' Clara refused to be beguiled. 'We need *money*. You can't go on just *giving* your work all the time.'

'I don't know — if it makes people happy —'

'What about *me*?'

Clara, accustomed since childhood to empty purses, felt the cold draught of poverty each time the bank statement arrived and she fretted dreadfully. Salisbury did not have it in him to worry about such matters. Money was something that went in at one pocket and out at the other. If you hadn't got enough to pay bills immediately people were pretty decent on the whole and didn't often mind waiting for settlement.

Nonconformist to the core, he always broke rules. Income tax? Insurance? Such complexities were not for him. His family said: 'There's one law for the rich and another for Pa!' He had his own way of doing everything — and he always thought his own way was incomparably the best way. The manner in which he played bridge, for instance — people were very cross with him because they said the way he led was against the rules. To which accusation Salisbury would gaily riposte that it was time the rules were changed. Although he was too gentle and affectionate ever to be an Angry Man, he was, nevertheless, a real rebel, genuinely anti-Establishment, a true anarchist.

'You've got everything you want, Clara,' he now said. 'You're quite safe. These children will be able to enjoy their party more now. Don't you see?'

He sympathized with that feeling of insecurity left over from her childhood, was sorry she still had a sense of inferiority in social life and he always did his genuine best to protect her.

'Well, I would like a maid.' Clara thought of all her friends whose front doors were opened by maids, who never had to do any washing-up.

'But you've got a maid, Clara.'

'You know she only stays until two o'clock.'

This was true. Granny, however, was thrilled by this daily char. She always tried to visit Clara early and she made as much mess as possible so that the maid would have plenty to do and be worth her wages, even imperiously sweeping the crumbs from the table to the floor after lunch for the maid to brush up.

'Dorothy has a living-in maid,' she added.

'Dorothy hasn't got a seaside cottage,' Salisbury reminded her firmly. 'Nor has Maud or Joyce. And they haven't got a car either. And I bet they none of them have such real fun as we do. You'd better go and get on with the packing. You'll feel better about everything when you're down at Clymping.'

'We'll have to make an early start,' said Clara, accepting Salisbury's arguments with good grace. 'We're picking up Granny on the way.'

Salisbury had sworn he would be the first of the family to own a car. And he had been, just getting in ahead of John, who had dawdled on the way, collecting other things first, such as wirelesses, women, radiograms, microscopes. Bernard and Dorothy liked their bicycles: Maud and Reggie had a taste for taxis.

The present car was Salisbury's third. They were always old and cheap and in need of attention, but this was exactly what this kind, sweet-natured man craved. His heart went out to things in distress; he loved putting them right, making things function properly. At the first sag of a gate or rattle of a window he would put aside the modelling and carving that now and then paid the bills and attend to the invalid. A friend had only to breathe — 'The frame of my wife's portrait has cracked —', a child to show him a broken toy, and he would instantly feel compelled to make and mend. He was a born contriver, a natural inventor. A craftsman of genius, there was nothing to which he could not turn his hand. In the studio he had cupboards crammed from floor to ceiling with treasures — boxes, tins, odd gloves, scraps of material, empty cotton reels, baskets, balls, insides of clocks, wires, screws — all the driftwood of living that he collected and hoarded because it might come in useful one day — you never knew —

Considering that Salisbury was perfectly equipped to make anything that was necessary with his own hands, it was really entirely logical that he should not worry about having money with which to buy things.

Granny sat in the back of Salisbury's car as they bowled home to the Clymping cottage after a shopping expedition. She was shelling peas into a colander on her lap and tossing the pods to left and right out of the window.

'So's they'll be ready to cook directly we get home,' she explained to Betty who was looking uneasily back at the empty pods stretching away behind them like the trail of some lugubrious paper chase. 'Mustn't waste time. Every minute's precious.'

One might have thought that now she had eight grandchildren with the eldest seventeen, she would have allowed time to relax. Not a bit of it! She continued to compete energetically against that old man with the scythe, cramming every day with activity. What were the days for if not to be used and worked in to their full extent? Idleness was still the deadliest of the sins, just as it had been in those distant years in the Potteries when they sat working round the table by lamplight during the long winter evenings and heard sinful drunken sluggards singing terrible songs as they staggered up the road outside their window.

The peas all done she whisked her knitting from her bag and as she plained and purled she talked about the tennis party they were having that afternoon.

'Are you sure we bought everything on the list, Betty? We mustn't be short of food. I'll have time to make two or three more cakes before lunch. Your mother's got shortbread and oatcakes and I made some raisin bread last night. I think I'll beat up some egg whites for meringues while the peas are cooking.'

'Wait till you see what *I*'ve made.' chuckled Salisbury. 'Just what we need for a tennis party!'

'Betty, love, you'll have time to make fudge before lunch.'

'I've got some sewing to finish, Granny.'

'Have you? Oh well, as long as you're occupied with something creative.'

'Wait till old battling Angus sees it! It's a real scream!' Salisbury tooted his horn exuberantly. 'By the way, Granny, did you know John rang up this morning?'

'All the way from London? That must have cost a lot.'

'He's motoring down this afternoon. With Annabella.'

'Can we possibly get in touch with Dorothy, do you think? And persuade her not to come?' Granny bit her lip anxiously. 'You know what she's like. I don't know what she'll say when she meets Annabella.'

'Dorothy'll be all right, Granny. Tennis always puts her in a good mood. Anyway, we are sort of giving this party in honour of old Bernard, aren't we. To celebrate his success.'

Bernard had recently been elected to the Royal Academy of Arts. He had officially arrived. He was at the top of his profession. Granny had almost wept with joy and pride when his election was announced. How pleased his father would have been! She hoped that perhaps, in that consciousness beyond life, he knew about it.

'Perhaps Dorothy'll have to go before Johnnie comes,' hoped Granny. 'She often does make excuses to leave early.'

Salisbury held out his arm to show he was turning right. 'Home at last!' he said. 'Lovely *home*!'

He drove carefully up the narrow drive to the cottage and drew up by the front door. Holding the colander of peas as carefully as a basket of eggs, Granny eased herself out of the back seat and calling out, 'Clara, Clara, the peas are ready — Have you got the water on to boil? — she went nimbly into the kitchen.

Betty deposited bags and baskets in the hall and went off into the sitting-room and settled down with her sewing before she could be told to lay the table.

Salisbury drove the car into the shade of the garage, wiped the hot dust from the bonnet and then decided that he had better go an inspect the tennis court again. He had already inspected it twice that morning — but you never knew — a bird might have entangled itself in the nets and need rescuing, or a cat walked along a white line while it was still wet.

This seaside cottage was Salisbury's declaration of independence and Granny's symbol of social status. To Clara it meant a lot of hard work. She could never finally make up her mind whether she was glad about having it or not: she was inclined to blame it for their lack of ready money.

Salisbury had decided to build the cottage on the spur of the moment, on the spur of a decree proclaiming that henceforth only land-owners would be entitled to use that particular stretch of shore. Salisbury himself had practically never used the beach there and he never bathed. It was the idea of not being allowed to do so if ever he should want to that infuriated him so much. Forbid Salisbury? Forbid the sun to rise. When he realized the only way round the prohibition was to become a land-owner himself he bought a plot of ground near the shore, designed a cottage, hired occasional local labour to help him build it and made the furniture and fittings himself, putting to use any good driftwood or other treasures that the sea might wash up on to the sand.

Granny had her own bedroom there and came to the cottage as often as possible. Things were all right again at Oxford Road. Joyce and Angus were living there now and Granny was happy and her old beaming self. Mollie had been pushed out and installed, most unhappily, in a flat in Chelsea. She refused to give Johnnie the divorce he asked for and did all she could to break up his love nest and get him back. The family wondered whether poor John would ever find peace and happiness. They all (except, of course, Dorothy, who was unconditionally on Mollie's side) liked Annabella and made much of her. She was an unassumingly elegant, gentle young woman and appeared devoted to John. As Mollie had done, she cooked delectable meals for him and saw to it that he had his daily helping of fresh shrimps and thin brown bread and butter. She was kind. She was musical. She and John sang duets together, John in his rich baritone and Annabella in a light soprano. The family thought John was quite lucky to have won such a prize. They regretted the necessity for him to live in sin; this was not their way at all. But once more it was all the fault of Mollie. They trusted the terrible woman would soon come to her senses and give John his freedom.

Prowling round the outside of the cottage, making sure everything was in order, Salisbury glimpsed Clara and Granny through the kitchen window. Granny was already mixing up cakes; she hadn't even stopped to take off her hat and coat. He grinned. What a woman! What energy! No one would think she was the wrong side of seventy. He was very fond of Granny and never minded having her around. He listened to her reminiscences with good humour, unstopped her sink, mended her broken sash cords. He and she were really two of a kind — creative, unorthodox, affectionate, gregarious.

He went along to the tennis court. He had won a *News-Chronicle* 'Ad-Cut' competition and received a useful sum of money as a prize; this had gone towards the making of the tennis court. Delighted by his success in the competition, he had sent in other entries under other names and had won two more prizes. The one attributed to Mrs. Annie Seabridge, of Oxford Road, Putney, had done particularly well and Granny had parted with the reward like a lamb, not even demanding a ten per cent cut. The other person had, however, to Salisbury's astonishment and disgust, refused to part with the money that came to him from the newspaper out of the blue.

The lines on the court were still unsmudged and as straight as rulers. No frail birds fluttered desperately in the net; no hole needed to be meticulously darned. The blazing sun was in its place in the heavens. Everything seemed to be in order.

But Salisbury scratched his bald head and reflected — some hard hitters would be coming this afternoon, battling Angus had been putting in a lot of practice recently and one or two of the children took such wild swipes that the balls went all over the place. He looked towards the cottage and decided he had better think of some way to protect the windows.

Betty, sewing on the sitting-room sofa, said 'Blast!' as a square of asbestos suddenly blocked out the daylight. 'What *are* you doing, Pa?'

'Battling Angus! Windows!'

'Bother Uncle Angus! I'm trying to finish the embroidery on my bathing-dress.'

She gathered up her sewing and went upstairs to the bedroom where she found Deborah pinning badges all over her dress.

'I say, you're not going to appear like *that*, are you?'

'What's wrong?' asked Deborah, calmly pinning a badge of the Ancient Order of Froth Blowers above her heart. She was an inveterate 'joiner' and belonged to any club that supplied a badge — Gug Nuncs, Dumb Friends League, Tiny Tims, League of Nations Junior —

'I mean to say — it's rather babyish. You are fourteen.

'Well, I like them!' Deborah clutched at her insignia and looked ready to cry. 'You know I'm not allowed to wear them at school.'

'Jolly good thing too.'

'You're just bad-tempered.'

'So'd you be if you had to spend half your life down in this beastly cottage.'

'But I do have to. And I like it.'

'It's all right for you. You're only a child. But I'm sick of it. Every week-end, every holidays — off we have to go down to the cottage. Think of all the fun we're missing.'

'What fun?'

'Well — er — theatres.'

'Mummy's always saying we can't afford to go to the theatre.'

'That's just it. We can never afford anything. We've been poor ever since Pa built the cottage. Remember that time he took us to the theatre twice in one week? In the stalls?'

'Anyway, it's nice for Granny,' murmured Deborah primly, echoing her elders.

'But we could spend the hols in exciting places. We could go abroad.'

'You did last year,' Deborah reminded her. 'To France. With Sarah.'

'Well, I'm bored with it all. I want to live my own life.'

'What sort of life?'

'You're too young to understand,' said Betty haughtily. 'Anyway why *should* I always have to say where I'm going and who with?' She bit off her embroidery thread and threw the bathing-dress on the bed. 'There, it's finished! Like it?'

Across the middle of the black stockinette costume a huge sun cast its beams down on a church with a steeple. The scene was colourful and bold. Betty was going through a very religious phase and she considered it right and proper that she should parade on the beach with the Christian church emblazoned on her breast.

'You're really going to wear it?' mused Deborah, fingering her humble little badges.

'Of course. This afternoon.'

'Who's coming?'

'Most of the family. Not Sarah though. She's abroad again — lucky pig! But Diana and —'

'I thought Diana was in a Nursing Home? Something wrong with her leg — t.b. or something?'

'You are out of date! She's been home ages now. She's at Art School. She's better.'

'Any locals coming?'

'Mummy's asked a few. There's a jolly decent boy staying with them next door and he's coming too. And do you know who else?'

'Who?'

'Uncle Johnnie's German girl,' said Betty, who had no sense of geography and thought that any part of Europe not France or Italy was probably Germany.

'Oh, her!' said Deborah coolly.

She was not yet alive to the follies of her elders. The scandals, the indignation, the talking and telephoning when the news broke that Mollie had made another scene, had followed Johnnie to Paris and waylaid him in the Champs-Élysées — it all drifted like mist round her consciousness. Their troubles were as distant as stars. She was a docile, affectionate child, easily frightened but with unexpected strength when she set her mind on anything. She adored their seaside weekends, loved the hard sunlight, the salty, sea-weedy smell, the feathery tamarisk hedges; she didn't know what Betty was making such a fuss about.

'Everyone's terrified what Auntie Dorothy's going to say,' went on Betty gleefully. 'I'm longing to see what'll happen. They haven't met before, you see. And Auntie Dorothy's awfully sedate. I think there'll be a terrific scene. I think —'

'Look out, girls!' Salisbury's head appeared above the window sill. The girls noticed the end of a ladder. 'Where was Moses when the light went out?'

'Blow!' said Betty, as another square of asbestos blocked out the sun. 'I wanted to powder my face. Anyway, I suppose we'd better make an appearance in the kitchen and see if we can help. Come on, Deborah. You can't get out of everything just because you're the youngest.'

They sat down to an early lunch in the blacked-out cottage, changed into tennis clothes, laid out the tea and waited for people to arrive.

Ralph came first.

Dorothy had been lent a cottage near Chichester, a charming, ramshackle place in the middle of an old orchard. Joyce and Angus were staying in a bungalow somewhere along the coast. For them all it meant a long bus ride and Granny filled several jugs with home-made lemonade and put out glasses ready to refresh the travellers.

Thankful the cramped journey was over, Ralph shrieked and whistled full speed ahead up the drive: he was an engine. Dorothy came next, burdened with macs, then Diana, who was carrying a basket of bathing things and walking as though her shoes were too tight, and a long way behind came Vicky carrying the rackets and telling herself a story.

'It looked like rain when we left,' explained Dorothy, putting down the Burberrys. 'I'd love a glass of cold water, Clara dear.'

'Where's Bernard?' asked Granny.

'He's coming on later. By himself, as usual.' Dorothy uttered the special, mirthless laugh she reserved for painful situations. 'Some of his friends turned up and he went sailing at Itchenor with them.'

'Oh dear, I hope he won't be long.'

Dorothy wished that Granny might at least make a pretence of being glad to see *her* instead of immediately expressing concern about her son. It was inconsiderate and unkind and made her wish she could leave the children there and go off by herself for a long walk among the golden cornfields that were rustling in the breeze. 'He'll come when he wants to,' she said, with another dry, bitter little laugh. She still found it impossible to resign herself to Bernard's inability to be a family man. The baby of her own family, petted and fussed by her own mother, no one had ever cold-shouldered her until she married into this clever, indomitable family. Bernard's evasions and disappearances depressed her very much, like an unjust punishment. She wandered away from her in-laws and began smelling the roses.

Joyce and Angus arrived soon after.

'Bruce has been terrible,' said Joyce, who looked hot and bothered. 'He always does the exact opposite of what we want him to do. We had to *drag* him off the bus. He wanted to go up on top.'

'Come to Granny, love!' She opened her arms wide.

Bruce glared at her, shook his curls and rushed away to join Ralph, who was hooting round and round the sundial.

'Never mind!' laughed Angus. 'He'll grow out of it. How is everybody?' He bestowed kisses all round. 'Anyone feel like a knock-up?'

'Let's recover from the journey first,' begged Joyce.

Angus was dressed up in white flannels and looked very handsome. When it came to sport he more than made up for any artistic deficencies he might have. Burly, cheerful, fair, he played games like a trained athlete. 'Dorothy's a sport —' he said, hardly able to wait to start playing. 'She'll give me a game.'

Half a dozen neighbours wandered in, including a woman half-hidden in a wide straw hat and two rosy young men who immediately attached themselves to Diana and Betty. Clara said, 'I suppose I'd better umpire,' and dutifully climbed up into the high seat Salisbury had made from an old step-ladder, Angus leapt backwards and forwards over the tennis net and Salisbury suddenly remembered his invention and ran back into the cottage, returning with a box that he rattled provocatively at everyone. 'It's a real brainwave! A breath saver!' he exclaimed. 'Just you wait and see!' Everyone waited, but he said, 'Presently, presently!' So fours were made up, play started and the spectators subsided into deck-chairs and fanned themselves with whatever they could find.

The rosy young men partnered the two girls first. The game was soon finished and they decided to go on to the beach and swim.

'Dorothy — you and I'll take on Joyce and Salisbury now,' said Angus.

117

This match proved to be very close; the games went on and on from deuce to deuce. Dorothy had a scorching service and played well; Joyce was unexpectedly quick and sure.

'She used to play hockey at school,' Granny proudly informed the neighbour in the cavernous hat.

'Reallaay — hockaay — How awfullaay brave!'

The indigenous Clympingites stretched their final syllables to grotesque lengths in the interests of polite pronunciation: it had become the local dialect.

Salisbury was a good net player, twisting and jumping like a frog. But it was Angus who won the gasps and bravos. Even Granny, watching him serve and volley and smash like a professional, forgot he could not draw, could not play the double-bass, could not design a chest of drawers or build a radio.

'Deuce!' said Clara for the umpteenth time.

'Go it, partner!' encouraged Angus.

He and Dorothy bent forward aggressively as Joyce prepared to serve.

Two balls went into the net. 'Oh, sorry partner!' said Joyce, crossing to the other court and trying again.

Her next service limped over: Dorothy reached it too late. 'Sorry partner!' she exclaimed.

'Deuce!' called Clara.

'What a deuced set this is!' Salisbury mopped his head. 'Now then, partner, a great effort!'

They made a great effort, but hit each other as Angus's volley whizzed between them.

'Never say die!' commented Salisbury, rubbing the place Joyce had hit.

Angus misjudged his strength with the next shot and banged the ball just out of court.

'Deuce!' yawned Clara.

'Oh, dear. *Sorry* partner!'

'What a polite familaay — extraordinaraay —

'The time has come,' said Salisbury, 'for my little surprise. Half a jiffy.'

'Hey, let's finish the game first, old chap,' called Angus as Salisbury left the court. Angus did not believe rules should be broken.

'There!' Salisbury opened the box and proudly handed round a number of strange badges, one for each person. 'Pin it on your front — like this — Now, you see this string?' He touched a string dangling from the badge. 'When you lose a point for your partner, all you need do is just pull the string. Like this. And — lo and behold —'

The front of the badge fell open revealing inside the large word SORRY.

'Saves your breath!' laughed Salisbury. 'So simple!'

As they all played with their new toys a car drove unnoticed up to the cottage and a loud voice silenced the merriment.

'Hullo! I hope we're not late for tea.'

'Johnnie!' Granny pushed herself out of her deck-chair. 'At last! And Annabella. How pretty you look, dear.'

'John and — that person,' breathed Dorothy. 'No — I wouldn't have come —'

'The game!' wailed Angus as even the umpire deserted the court. 'Dorothy —' he appealed to his partner standing in shocked immobility.

'Let you and I play a single, Angus,' she suggested rather sternly.

She would certainly not have made the tiring journey had she known that they were to be of the party. Their arrival made her feel faint. She could not understand how such a basically decent, sober-living family could bring themselves to entertain this woman who had broken up the marriage of Johnnie and Mollie. Her cheeks flamed. She thought that the way they had treated Mollie was unforgiveable. Indignation revived her.

'Let's play for service, shall we, Angus?'

She slashed the ball across the net. It was all very immoral and it set a bad example to the young ones. Diana was quite silly enough about boys already. Where was Diana anyway? She looked about her and lost the point.

'Let's have that one again,' said Angus kindly.

'All right.'

She began to play with ominous concentration, like a gathering storm, and she almost managed to beat the battler.

Trouble came at tea-time.

Nearly everyone was tired and happy. The little boys had dressed themselves up in seaweed and were in a lovely mess, the girls and the young men had bathed, the women had made the tea and the uncles walked about smoking and talking shop.

There was an abundance of food, in the best family tradition. All the old-established favourites were there — the oatcakes, the raisin bread, the rich soggy cakes; Granny's meringues were a miracle of sweet lightness and Clara had even made sardine sandwiches for John, who liked these next best to shrimps.

Bernard had still not arrived; Dorothy felt unable to join in the general animation. Her moods came and went quickly and she was now assailed by a feeling of inferiority and loneliness, a conviction that she did not really belong in this capable, worldly circle, that she could not equal any of them in talents and abilities. She wished she could become invisible; it was the same sort of foolish wish that used sometimes to overcome her at the smart parties she attended with Bernard, where it seemed to her that everyone was better dressed and more accomplished than she, where she often used to wander away and find books to look at rather than make conversation with people who didn't seem interested in her. Melancholy began to seep up in her, with its usual companion — irritation. She looked round the table. Everyone seemed to be laughing and making a lot of noise. John had just passed his cup up for about the seventh refill, saying as he did so, 'Another cup of tea for Mrs. Whitehouse, please.' Diana was actually sitting by the side of Annabella and talking to her. Diana had on too much make-up. When was the child going to stop ruining her appearance? Dorothy had never used cosmetics in her life and she both feared and despised women who did.

She stared across the table until Diana became conscious of her mother's regard.

'Too much lipstick!' Dorothy mouthed the words. 'Rub it off!'

No one could have heard, but Diana fancied everyone did; she blushed and frowned, dabbed at her mouth with her handkerchief and went on talking to Annabella, who she thought was very sweet, so warm and sympathetic.

'I 'ave a dress at 'ome I sink would feet you,' the young Austrian woman was saying. 'We are about zee same size. *Ja?* Would you like to come to zee flat one day for zee tea. And we try zee dress. *Ja?*'

'I'd love to.'

'I vill ask your Onkel to arrange et. Yes?'

In spite of the cordiality with which she was always welcomed by John's family, Annabella felt constrained. Her position was difficult. She loved her kind, fat Englishman who was always so generous to her. She wanted to be safely married to him and would not have left her home in Vienna unless it had seemed certain that he was going to marry her. Those awful scenes when that Mollie woman jumped out at them round street corners and shouted made her feel sick with terror. She was sometimes afraid to be alone in the flat. Now and then she almost wished she had never met John. A girl-friend had persuaded her to go to Sacher's Rote Bar one evening, just for fun, and see who they met. There she met Johnnie, passing through Vienna, and it all turned out to be more serious than she had anticipated. She came from a respectable family and she did not really want to live like this. How, she sometimes asked herself, had it all come to pass. Perhaps it was the war, that terrible war. Conditions in Austria were so difficult: in winter they were often so cold and hungry. Her dear, funny Englishman was so good to her and her family, so *mitfühlend* and *gemütlich* and it had seemed to her that life in England would promise warmth and riches.

'When I go along in Kensington High Street,' Dorothy broke her silence, needing an argument to bring relief to her personal tensions, 'and I see all the beggars standing in the gutter —'

'In Vienna too,' murmured Annabella. 'We 'ave such people.'

'I got such a bargain at Pontings' Sale,' remembered Granny, to whom Kensington High Street meant Barkers, Derrys and Pontings. 'Ever such a smart coat for five shillings.'

'— and on Sundays, when the starving miners sing in the streets,' went on Dorothy, 'and the little ragged children —'

'I do wonder what's happened to Bernard,' said Clara nervously.

'— then I think to myself,' continued Dorothy, following an unswerving line, 'it's time for a revolution.'

'You're a damn fool!' Johnnie could not resist the temptation. 'You don't know what you're talking about. Revolution indeed! Now, there's a man coming up in Germany, a little Austrian corporal, who's really talking sense about unemployment.'

'Hitler,' said Dorothy. 'Oh yes, I've heard all about Hitler. He's —'

'He's got some sense in his head. He knows what to do with all the damn bolshies. I've met a lot of business people in Germany — important business people — big men — who believe Hitler'll put the country to rights again. They think he'll be the next Chancellor.'

'Hitler's a terrible person,' said Dorothy very quietly.

'Dorothy, you don't know anything about Hitler.'

'I read the papers, John.'

'Then you read the wrong papers. You're a fool, Dorothy. You and your damn Russians.'

'I say,' whispered the young man by Diana's side. 'We're having a party this evening. Do you think you could come?'

'I don't know. I'll have to ask.'

'I'm beginning to think,' declared Dorothy, 'that communism is the only way for mankind to be saved. The Russian revolution was inevitable. It was a hope for the rest of us.'

'*Dorothy!*' John was red in the face. 'You're *mad*! They're a lot of bloody-minded Jews, those bolshie bandits. I was there, Dorothy, *there*. I saw the pools of blood on the snow. Mollie and I —'

'Bernard! There's Bernard!' cried Granny joyfully.

123

'We were just talking about you, Bernard, bless you.'

'It didn't sound very friendly,' said Bernard wag-gishly.

'Have my chair, old chap!' Angus stood up.

'How's the Royal Academy?' Salisbury looked proudly at his brother-in-law. 'Have the new letters after your name brought in a nice lot of fat commissions?'

'As a matter of fact,' said Bernard ruefully, 'the amount of work's fallen off since I was elected. I was doing quite nicely before. Other people have told me they had exactly the same experience.'

'How did the sailing go?' asked Clara.

'Have a piece of cake, dear,' said Joyce.

They could all have hugged him for arriving when he did. Dear, convenient, clever Bernard.

'Well then, if you can't get work — down with the Royal Academy.' said Salisbury. 'Down with tradi-tional art!'

'You don't mean that?' queried Granny anxiously.

'Of course I don't. It's only the failures who sneer at Burlington House, the types who can't get a picture hung and then pretend they wouldn't touch the Academy with a barge pole. Sour grapes! I'd be thrilled if they elected me. What about this tennis badge as a Diploma work, Bernard? A new modern kind of sculpture. Constructional with utilitarian under-tones. Do you think you could use your influence, dear boy? No, all the ones who really *know* about art are elected to the Academy — Constable, Gainsborough, Munnings, John, Gill, Zoffany — the lot. You're in good company, dear boy.'

'There is a slump,' reflected Bernard. 'We're all affected by economic conditions. It may not be the R.A.'s fault.'

'You'll have to do more teaching,' said John. 'Like Reggie.'

'Remember old Reggie's marching song?' laughed Salisbury. He seized Clara's hat, put it on at a jaunty angle and, tripping up and down like a music hall artist, sang:

> 'We are the old headmasters,
> Which is so very funny;
> We cannot paint, we cannot draw,
> But we earn a lot of money.'

'Join in everyone,' beamed Granny. 'A sinG-sonG!'

Everyone was melting away, however. The behatted neighbour, murmuring 'Frightfullaay sorraay,' had taken her leave, scared by the vehemence of the argument, Betty and Diana had disappeared with the two young men to listen to gramophone records, Dorothy had taken Vicky for a stroll along the beach.

'What a bourgeois lot they are!' she muttered. 'Not a thought beyond self-interest and bargain sales and the family. No *real* feeling for the plight of others. It's not enough.'

She stopped and gazed out at the quiet horizon. Little waves lapped about her plimsoles.

'How I wish I could find some great cause to live for,' she said. 'How I hate my petty self sometimes.'

'Do you?' Vicky did not understand what she meant but she sensed some unspeakable trouble in her mother and wanted to do something to help and protect her.

'Some great movement that will raise humanity to a higher level. Something that will make life better for the millions who are born without hope of happiness. Love is important. Yes, love is very important. But it is not enough.'

'No?' From an early age Vicky was her mother's confidante. This often made her feel very old and foisted on her an emotional responsibility that she did not really want.

They walked on a little farther. The influence of the calm surroundings, the sweet evening sky and the contented groups of people on the sands, gently returned Dorothy to a mood of serene charity. When she rejoined the family and suggested to Bernard that perhaps it was time to go home she did not even flinch when he replied, 'But I've only just come, my dear. You and the children had better go on ahead.'

She merely replied quietly, 'As you say, darling.'

'Can I come home when Daddy does?' Diana clutched at this straw of freedom, longing for an evening with the boys.

'No, dear. I shall want your help getting the supper and putting Ralph to bed.'

'*Please*. Just this once.'

'She'll be quite all right, Dorothy,' put in Clara.

'Come along, dear. Do as I say,' insisted Dorothy.

'I've come across *the* book for me, Johnnie,' said Bernard. 'Just the very book. By one of your Germans — Oswald Spengler. He puts the whole vast, complex situation in a nutshell. And *how* he can write! Listen to this —' He pulled out a sketch book, leafed through it.

As Dorothy took leave of everyone and trudged off with the macintoshes, the wet bathing things, the rackets and the tired, cross children, she heard Bernard start to quote from the book that was to become his Bible, the philosophy he was to expound on innumerable occasions during the years ahead as Europe rearmed and ideologies clashed in every country.

'We live,' he was reading, 'in one of the mightiest ages in all history, and no one sees, no one realizes —

Night has set in, the earth trembles and streams of lava are rolling down over entire nations — and we send for the fire-brigade.'

'Why wouldn't you let me stay?' Diana, silent during the long bus ride, raked up her grievances as they traipsed along the country lane towards their cottage.

'We won't go into all that again.'

'You never let me have any fun.'

'You know that's not true, darling. We love you very much and we want you to enjoy yourself. But you have been ill, sweetheart, and we don't want you to get overtired.'

'Betty says they're all going to Austria soon. Uncle Johnnie's invited them. Why can't I go too?'

'Don't ask silly questions.'

'Well, can I at least go and have tea at Uncle Johnnie's flat. I have been invited.' Diana knew what the answer would be but, perversely, could not help touching the wounds.

'For goodness' sake, Diana, be sensible. You worry me very much when you talk like this.'

'Well, you worry me, too. I think Annabella's perfectly sweet.'

'She's a home-breaker. It's a terrible thing to break up someone's home. She took your Uncle Johnnie away from your Auntie Mollie.'

'Perhaps he wanted her to take him away. Perhaps he couldn't bear it any longer. I think you're horrid.'

'*Silence!* That's enough. You're only a child.'

That night Vicky heard Diana crying in bed. She made no attempt to comfort her. Several years separated them and, age apart, they had little in common and were not close in any way. Diana loved clothes, dancing, make-up, boys. Vicky still liked things like kites, bows and arrows, pogo-sticks; she cared much more for her little brother than for her sister, and would often creep up to his bed when he was asleep and sit looking at him thinking what a very pretty little boy he was with his fair skin and delicate features.

'Do stop crying,' she said rather crossly to Diana. 'You're keeping me awake.'

'You don't understand,' cried Diana. 'No one understands what it's like.'

CHAPTER SEVEN

About two years later Diana's life reached a climax.

Johnnie's German business friends had, of course, been proved correct and Hitler was now dealing with unemployment and other matters in his own revolting style. The family did all they could to prevent John and Dorothy meeting face to face; their arguments roared like furnaces. Dorothy had recently begun to apply herself seriously to the study of Marx and she was now completely convinced that communism was the only good answer to economic problems. Bernard, backed up by Gibbon's *Decline and Fall* and Spengler's *Decline of the West*, was persuading himself (and trying to persuade others) that present events were inevitable, that the power of western civilization was doomed and was in its prolonged death throes, and he went on quoting, 'We are experiencing a volcanic eruption that is without parallel. Night has set in and the earth trembles —' Salisbury and Clara continued to play bridge; Reggie and Maud charmed all and sundry with their delightful looks and manners; Mollie, determined to get her man back, was still trailing John across Europe, from conference to conference, and up and down the Tottenham Court Road.

Perceptive collectors were quietly acquiring Ben Nicholsons and Henry Moores; Auden, Spender and the other young poets were in a ferment; Thomas Beecham was electrifying audiences at the Queen's Hall, Gielgud and Olivier were doubling as Romeo and Mercutio at the Old Vic, the beautiful Irene Scharrer was showing that no one could play Chopin's *Revolutionary Study* with such brilliant fervour, more and more people were finding out about Marie Stopes and free love was growing safer. The dreams of Hollywood were influencing the entire world; melancholy crooners clutched at microphones and moaned:

> 'Can't go on —
> Got no joy in life at all,
> Stormy weather —
> Since my love and I ain't together
> Keeps raining all the time —

The younger children were happy at their schools. Vicky and Ralph, having to find some way of exercising their spirit of adventure, roamed like cats over the flat roofs of the studios in the Lane: looking down through skylights, they watched James Gunn painting fashionable portraits, Charles Wheeler carving torsos, a popular novelist pacing about his study dictating romances to his secretary.

Betty was studying to be an architect, Sarah had just finished at Art School and was embarking on a career of textile designing, Diana, too, had just finished at Art School and was working in a dress shop.

Diana was a gentle, sensitive person: for her there had been no age without grace — she had changed from a pretty child into a lovely girl. Granny doted on her, the first grandchild to nestle in her eager lap, Sarah and Betty were her bosom friends, her parents thought the world of her and did everything they could to help her towards a happy, steady life. She had all kinds of natural advantages.

But things were far from well with her.

Later, when the blow fell, everyone wondered what on earth could have gone wrong, when it could all have started; they dug back into their memories trying to tease out some small detail that might have forewarned them. She used to sleep-walk sometimes, they said, as though she had some great anxiety on her mind; now and again she became rather hysterical and when she lost her temper the violence of her feelings was un-expected and a little shocking coming from such an apparently gentle person. Such occurrences, however, were really nothing out of the ordinary; all girls had to go through a silly season and let loose some of the fever of living within them. And, of course, it must have been very trying and unpleasant for her having to spend so many months in that Nursing Home far out in the country with her left leg encased in plaster right up to the hip — this must have robbed her of a lot of self-confidence and been a serious set-back.

All the same, what happened was impossible, almost unbelievable.

And because the burden of guilt had to be settled somewhere it was perfectly natural for many people to blame her parents, and particularly Dorothy, the mother always being held most responsible in such matters. She should, they said, have tried to understand her daughter better, have been more tolerant and less high-principled; should not, for instance, have regarded with such scorn Diana's passion for clothes and appear-ances; should not have condemned as naughtiness her timid explorations of the fringes of love.

It must have been very difficult for people who grew

up and fell in love before the slaughter of the 1914–18 War changed so many aspects of social life almost unrecognizably to come to terms with the new sexual freedom of the twenties and thirties. It needed a basic reassessment of moral values, the establishment of a different set of standards. Some people found it altogether impossible to adapt themselves to the manners of the new age. Dorothy had nothing of the coquette in her nature: she tried to bring up her daughters to distrust and spurn the impulses of the flirt and never to allow any man to take liberties with them. She was the sort of woman who probably had only one overwhelming devotion in her life and would never allow any other than her one true love even to kiss her. She was strict in a way that often seemed prim and proper, she was a puritan — but she was also a romantic who both revered and feared Aphrodite. Love to her was something infinitely precious, sacred and powerful; any form of flirtation, any tampering with emotions was, to her way of believing, pernicious and decadent, selfish and very dangerous. Let people love, by all means, let them be passionate and abandon themselves in the service of love — but let it not be those idle experiments of curiosity that ruined all capacity for deep, true feeling, that corrupted the springs of life. Anything that verged on promiscuity was, like luxury, abhorrent to her.

So she probably had not got it in her to do otherwise than take Diana's innocent nineteen-year-old flirtations very seriously. It worried her terribly that her daughter went out dancing in night clubs, often came home late, gave good-night kisses on the doorstep and had a succession of boy-friends. Diana was taken to task, urged to behave in a more dignified way, quite possibly made to feel obscurely guilty, to feel that she was not much good in one way and another, what with being ill and only working in a dress shop and so on.

However, she longed to get married and in spite of her great lack of self-confidence (or perhaps because of it) she dreamed endlessly of mutual love and joy.

Her dreams presently took shape.

He was a quiet, small, plain young man from an orthodox Jewish family. He was not an artist, he was not especially talented in any way; he was, in fact, rather dull. But he was warm and he was kind in an unprecedented degree. He never teased or mocked; he seemed to understand her. Her whole nature opened out to him; she felt safe. She lost her heart to him and for many months was happy.

Dorothy, stirring a custard for lunch, heard a tapping on her kitchen window and glanced up.

'Bother!' she exclaimed. 'Granny again! Why can't she send a postcard to say she's coming! I suppose it's money again.'

'I've been ringing and ringing,' complained Granny when Dorothy opened the door.

'I'm sorry, Granny, the bell's broken.'

'You should have a knocker, Dorothy. And that chair — out there in the middle of the Lane — I tumbled over it, Dorothy. It's dangerous. Shall I bring it in for you.'

'No, Granny, I put it out there to stop cars driving so fast down the Lane.'

'I gave myself ever such a knock on it.'

'It's terribly dangerous the way the cars come by so fast. Anyone might just step out of the front door and be underneath one. Ralph might easily rush out of the door when he's pretending to be Attila leading the Huns.'

'I saw Ralph playing right out in the road as I came through the Square,' Granny followed Dorothy into the kitchen and seated herself at the table. 'He was all dressed up like a Chinaman, bless him.'

'He loves that little hat and tunic I made him. Won't take them off! Even tries to go to bed in them!'

'Bless him! But Dorothy, is it all right for him to be playing out in the streets? I mean, just think —' and she thought of all the common children he might mix with out there in the rough and tumble of the road, children who might contaminate and spoil him.

'No, of course it's not all right, Granny,' replied Dorothy sharply, thinking of the fast cars and careless drivers who might not see the gay, wild little boy darting about in his Chinese tunic and embroidered hat. 'I worry all the time. But he's got to play *somewhere* — he's got to let off all his energy. If he plays in the Lane I get complaints from all these artistic people — all these painters and writers and people who say he makes too much noise. Do you know, there's one writer down the Lane, a fussy, fat man who writes popular rubbish, who came storming up to the kitchen window one morning and said that Ralph needed a flogging. Just imagine that — a flogging! And he was only running about outside with a sheet over him pretending to be a ghost.'

'Oh dear!'

'And if he plays indoors then Bernard complains of the noise and says it disturbs *his* work. These artists! And I can't always be taking him out for walks to Kensington Gardens and the Natural History Museum. Can I? I mean, someone's got to be at home to cook and mend and look after the famous sculptor, haven't they?'

'Yes,' agreed Granny, perplexed.

'And we can't afford a Nanny or anything like that. Anyway, we haven't any room.'

'Why isn't he at school today, Dorothy?'

'It's half-term.'

'Have you thought of sending him to boarding-school?'

'I've thought of everything.'

'Oh.'

'I want him to spend his youth with fields and trees round him. I want him to have living-space. It'll have to be boarding-school by hook or by crook when he gets a bit older. He must have grass to run about on. That's what really matters. Let's hope he'll be clever and get a scholarship somewhere.'

'I'm sure he will. All my children get scholarships.' Granny took off her hat and undid the buttons of her coat. 'You know, Dorothy, when I woke up this morning I thought how much I wanted to come and see Bernard again. So I got on a train and here I am. I love acting on sudden impulses, don't you? And I left myself enough time to do a bit of shopping in Kensington High Street too. Look at this pretty lace. It's a bit shop-soiled so it's reduced. Ever so cheap.'

'We haven't got a great deal for lunch today, Granny. I wish you'd send a postcard to tell us when to expect you.'

'But if I sent a postcard, Dorothy, then I wouldn't have the pleasure of suddenly making up my mind, would I?'

She began to fidget and she put on her hat again. 'Of course, if you don't want me, Dorothy, I could go and see if Maud's at home. Yes, I could catch a forty-nine bus. You see, I'm all alone today —' her voice wavered pitifully. 'Joyce is out and Clara's expecting visitors, so I didn't think I'd bother her. But I expect Maud —'

'For heaven's sake, Granny, of *course* we're glad to see you.'

'Is Bernard in?' she asked quickly, removing her hat again. 'Can I pop into the studio and see him?'

'He may have a model,' hedged Dorothy, who knew it put Bernard in a bad mood to be interrupted at his work, especially when the interruption was accompanied by the cold blast of a request for money. 'Anyway, you'll see him at lunch.'

'Well then, I'll just go upstairs and make myself comfortable and then I'll help you get the lunch.'

'*People!*' said Dorothy to herself as she emptied the custard into a jug and began to peel some more potatoes to put into the stew.

'Your piano, Dorothy! Your piano!' Granny returned to the kitchen in a state of agitation.

'We sold it to make room for a sofa. The sitting-room's small enough already and when Bernard entertains important clients in the house they must sit somewhere. They can't just drape themselves over the piano.'

'But the children, Dorothy. You can't deprive the children of music.'

'They didn't want to go on learning, Granny. They wouldn't. I couldn't just stand over them, could I? I couldn't *make* them practise. I mean, there's Bernard to look after.'

'I made my children. I stood over them.'

Dorothy started to sing to herself. Granny could be rather irritating at times.

'And Bernard'll miss the piano, too,' continued Granny. 'He had such a touch — really gifted. Bernard and Johnnie were both of them truly musical. They played beautifully. I remember how they once had a very difficult piece. Brahms, I think it was. Well, they decided they'd better tackle it together. So Bernard played the bass with both hands and dear little Johnnie did the treble with both his. And do you know — there was a lady passing by in the street and she heard them. And she knocked on the front door and she said, "Who's the genius playing the piano?" Yes, she said that.' Granny sighed. 'Oh, they did play so beautifully.'

'Well,' countered Dorothy, keeping her end up. 'Vicky sits on the sofa and she learns lots of poems by heart. Long poems, like *The Revenge*. And she recites them. And she came top in a school competition recently. The examiner said she'd never heard "Shall I compare thee to a summer's day" recited with such feeling and understanding.'

"Perhaps she'll take it up professionally,' suggested Granny. 'Be a diseuse.'

'I hope not. The theatre world's full of nasty people.'

Granny stayed all the afternoon. She did take Ralph out for a walk, but it was of short duration because he gave her the slip while she was cogitating over the pillow-cases in Barker's windows and ran home. She was upset about it and sat on the sofa breathing hard and saying that Joyce's Bruce and Jocelyn would never, never have been so naughty. Dorothy fed her with potted-meat sandwiches and cups of tea and she presently calmed down sufficiently to offer to help with the darning.

'How's Diana?' she asked. 'When I saw her last week at Maud's I thought she looked a bit peaky. And she was very quiet. You don't think she's going to be ill again, do you?' The swift illness that had carried off her husband had scarred her indelibly; if any of the family seemed off-colour she immediately felt a pang of terror.

'I hope not,' replied Dorothy, tense with sudden anxiety at the possibility of new frailty in her daughter.

'I think she's just been having too many late nights. Naughty little girl.'

'As long as that's all it is. Has she still got that same young man? The dark one who wears glasses?'

'I hope not.'

'Why not? He seemed quite a nice young man. Rather common, perhaps, but kind and considerate.'

'He's not doing her any good, Granny. He's got much more money than Diana's used to and he's introducing her to an idle lot of rich people who seem to spend most of their lives in night clubs. It's not the right sort of life for her. He's making her vain and silly. Bernard and I have felt very worried about it and we've told her she's to stop seeing him.'

'Oh dear — poor little Diana. But I thought he was serious about her. Wanted to marry her.'

'It's a love-affair that can't come to anything, Granny. He's from a Jewish family. Very strictly Jewish.'

'That wouldn't matter, would it? Jews make good family men.'

'It might not matter to us. But it would matter to his family. Orthodox Jews don't allow mixed marriages. Diana knows that. She knows he won't marry her. She's being a silly little fool about it and Bernard and I are having a very trying time with her. She's being most disobedient.' Dorothy's face was drawn as she talked and her voice sounded almost harsh with worry. There were qualities in Diana that she found hard to understand and she sometimes had to stretch her imagination painfully to grasp what was going on in her daughter's mind.

'Give her time, give her time,' said Granny gently. 'She's young and pretty. She'll meet someone else and soon get over this.'

'I hope so, Granny. I hope so.'

Diana came home late for supper that evening. When she appeared Granny was already on her second helping of pudding. She looked very pale and her eyes were red. Once or twice she did make an effort to join in the conversation but she soon lost the thread and appeared unable to concentrate. In fact she seemed altogether so strange and distraught that Dorothy, worried by a sense of foreboding and puzzled by behaviour that was completely outside her own experience, told her very sharply that if she couldn't pull herself together she'd better leave the room and go up to bed. Diana collected her scattered thoughts sufficiently to remain at table and later to see Granny off on her homeward journey, walking with her as far as Earls Court Station.

'How's the job?' asked Granny as they walked slowly along under the flowering lime trees.

'Oh — er — not too bad, I suppose.'

'Do you ever do any drawing and painting now? You used to do such nice little sketches, I remember.'

'Not often.'

'Perhaps you'll take up dress design.'

'Perhaps I will.'

'Betty's doing well with her architecture. And little Deborah's decided she'll take it up too. Isn't that nice!'

'Yes.'

'They're clever girls. Always making something original. Betty's got ever such a nice young man now. He took her to a lovely party last week.'

'Oh.'

'And a very rich young man asked Sarah to marry him a little while ago. But she said no. I hope she'll settle down soon. She's been invited to the country this week-end by some friends. They're very rich and they've got a large estate.'

'Did he? Has she? Oh — yes —'

Diana wondered how her cousins managed to find these suitable young men. Were they much prettier than she was? Were they more charming, easier to get on with? She wondered what it was about them that made rich young men propose, and why she didn't get invited away to large estates in the country for the week-end, and why her parents so often objected to her choice of friends and told her not to be so silly, and why it was that Jews wouldn't allow their sons to marry Gentile maidens, and if this really was the truth or just a convenient excuse, and why it was that her heart felt so leaden that she found difficulty in moving, why it was that everything seemed to be closing in around her so that she could hardly see, hardly hear — What was that Granny was saying —

'Sorry, Granny, what did you say?'

'I said doesn't this dust get up your nose. We need a shower of rain to settle it. I'm sure you'll soon meet a nice young man, love. I'm sure everything'll soon come right. He's just round the corner waiting for you.'

That was all nonsense — she had met a nice young man and everything had not gone right. What did she lack in herself? Was she really just a silly little fool, like her mother sometimes said when she got very cross with her? She wished she could talk, explain, confide in some kind, wise person who'd lived through something like this themselves. But her tongue didn't seem to belong to her; it refused to speak the words she was thinking, and in any case words were not enough. Was there no one who could show her what to do, who could guide her through this darkness where everything was beginning to hurt and frighten her?

In story books grandmothers sat in rocking-chairs and gave love and good advice to children in trouble. They had warm, soft shoulders on which to weep;

they had simple infallible cures for unhappiness. Granny — help me — help — Rock me to sleep and when I wake up let this pain be gone —

But it was too late, too late. She could not bring herself to cry out and already they had reached the station. Granny was blowing her nose and fumbling in her purse for the fare. She kissed Diana fondly, gave her a searching, anxious look and told her to be a dear, sensible girl and have a nice early night for a change.

Some weeks later, after a period of storms, tears, misunderstandings, Bernard and Dorothy arranged a small evening gathering of friends for her, hoping somehow to help her get over this love-affair that had gone wrong.

But despair had already overwhelmed Diana's frail defences. She felt too sick at heart to be present at her party and she went to bed instead. During that night she decided that she didn't want to go on living any longer.

The whole family was shaken to the roots. It was an inconceivable thing to happen. Granny aged visibly. Dorothy never forgave herself, although she did not know just where she had failed, what she had left undone. Vicky was disturbed for years.

But though tragedy is strong, life is stronger. The weeks and months went by, the torment diminished, a sense of proportion returned. Charity replaced accusation.

Bernard turned to his beautiful stone world of grace and harmony with redoubled zeal: Dorothy championed the cause of the underprivileged and unlucky with added fervour. Every year, on Diana's birthday, Bernard gave Dorothy a bunch of white roses, but they never spoke about it together, never a word. This silence, with its tremendous depths and undercurrents of feeling, was a great power in that household, shaping and directing the life of each individual member with its strong influence.

Actually, no one in the family talked about it very much: there was really nothing that could be said. But people often gave it thought. The ways of destiny are strange and subtle and perhaps the memory of Diana may have made them more perceptive, more compassionate. It may even have influenced Mollie and Johnnie, made them pause in their strident, recriminating, self-absorbed ways and wonder if perhaps it was time they stopped carrying on like that.

CHAPTER EIGHT

I⊤ seemed as though it were the sisters-in-law who were bearing the brunt of that driven, ambitious childhood in Beaufort Street.

Mollie had been pushed out of the jealously guarded domestic circle; Dorothy gradually withdrew of her own accord after Diana's death. Bernard called on Granny now and then, when he could spare the time from his work and he was always gentle and courteous. But it would be many years before Dorothy could bring herself to be easy with the family again, before she could find the confidence to demolish the barrier, that had sprung up around her — a barrier of pride, pain, self-defence, remorse.

Johnnie kept on breezing in and out of the house in Oxford Road, bestowing kisses and compliments, warming Granny with his exuberance and sentimentality. Very often on Sunday afternoons he brought his Annabella to take tea with her. In the summer they sat out in the garden and Annabella would depart with her arms full of generous, fragrant bunches of flowers. In the winter they enjoyed the luxury of drawing-room tea, their three arm-chairs drawn close to one of Granny's roaring fires, dishes of crumpets and hot buttered scones keeping warm on the hearth. Granny found a willing audience; Annabella seemed to enjoy listening to her tales and would sit attentively, her pretty head held slightly sideways on her slender neck, her eyes bright with humour and intelligence.

She told Annabella how she travelled all the way to Russia before the 1914–18 War, to visit Johnnie, who was in residence in Moscow. It had been exciting going all the way across Europe in the great Trans-European express. Everyone had been so kind to her, so thoughtful. And Moscow —

'Oh, Annabella, the parties, the parties! We had such fun! And the food, Annabella, the food! Have another scone, dear. That's right. And another cup of tea? Everyone was so kind to me. And do you know — I always had some work in my hands of course, at all the parties, and some of the Russian ladies used to ask for my patterns — I had to explain that I made them up as I went along. But there was one lady who was doing a beautiful piece of crocheting and it was my turn to ask for the pattern. And do you know what she said? She said she'd give me the pattern if in return I'd give her my recipe for looking so young. Wasn't that nice of her. Nobody ever believes me when I tell them how old I am. I suppose it's leading such a busy life!'

She told her stories many times, sometimes delving right back into the past to her Staffordshire childhood when she had skated to school along the frozen canals (no one such a swift skater as she once she had learned the way) when she had played hopscotch in the back yard, when she had stood outside the pubs singing to the poor, befuddled men of 'water, crystal clear', terrified of their rough ways, but determined to see it through.

144

'And now, Annabella love, let's have some music. You and Johnnie sing something in German, will you. How about a duet from *The Merry Widow*? Yes? Now just let me find the music and I'll play the accompaniment. Here we are. Now then — *one*, two, three, *one*, two, three —'

Yes, those were happy afternoons, the two voices mingling in some gay Viennese song, the firelight playing on the walls. Granny was so pleased that Johnnie was happy with Annabella and she hoped that their relationship would soon be made legal. She had no idea that Johnnie was still leading rather a double life, that he sometimes called to see Mollie and accepted the shrimps and the brown bread and butter she provided to welcome him. Granny was still expecting that Mollie would soon give him a divorce.

The three sisters knew of John's visits, however, and they were not very hopeful of a divorce. The three sisters knew most things. Clara, so dutiful and precise, a little, round woman with a passion for order and for doing things properly — Joyce, whose capacity for kindness and hospitality was becoming a family legend — Maud, whose beauty, like a suit of magic armour, protected and enhanced her so that she led a charmed, precious life — they were all three on good terms with one another. They were cross with each other sometimes and Maud often irritated her plainer, less selfish sisters beyond endurance, but basically they were close and fond. Granny had united as well as driven them. Their loyalty and devotion to her was absolute and it was undoubtedly her central presence that bound them together in a good relationship.

The sisters cultivated the grape-vine, chatting and back-chatting about family affairs, passing on all their gleanings. News buzzed from telephone to telephone.

'Do you know, Mollie actually had the nerve to beard Johnnie in his office! Yes, she did! She stormed into the building and made such a fuss they had to fetch him from an important conference in the board-room.'

'How tewwible!'

'And Johnnie told Salisbury that Mollie sometimes rings up Annabella and shouts threats at her. The poor girl's quite frightened to answer the telephone.'

'No— '

'Weggie says Bernard's got a commission to do a memowial to Sir Alfwed Gilbert. In St. Paul's.'

'That ought to be well paid. Do you remember when we were all little, being invited to tea in Sir Alfred's studio? Mother dressed us all up in our best.'

'Bernard's always so pessimistic nowadays. Weally gloomy.'

'I suppose it's understandable. Poor Bernard. Have you seen that lovely posthumous head he carved of Diana? It made the tears come to my eyes. It's so poignant and tender.'

'Weggie sees him quite often at the Chelsea Arts Club and he says Bernard's always talking about that German philosopher of his. And he says the Bwitish Empire's falling in wuins and Hitler's going to destwoy us all but it's all quite inevitable —'

'No — oh, poor Bernard.'

'That's what Weggie says he says. Bernard says the same thing happened to the Woman Empire. I'm afwaid it's all too learned for me.'

'Well, I think it's all Dorothy's fault.'

'What, dear, the fall of the Empire?'

'You know how she is. Always against the Government and the Royal Family. She won't even stand up

146

for *God Save the King*. Granny went to a concert with her and Dorothy just sat and fidgeted when they played the Anthem.'

'How embawwassing!'

'Have you heard? Johnnie's bought Mollie a house to keep her quiet. A big house. With a garden.'

'Goodness, he must be getting awfully rich. Where?'

'Kingston.'

'Let's hope it does keep her quiet.'

'And he's bought her a dog. Something to love. A great Airedale.'

'Well — I don't know — I think he just ought to drop her.'

'But, dear, she always bounces up again!'

'Johnnie's so sentimental. He's like a great, soft jelly wobbling about between the two women.'

'Granny said Vicky asked her the other day if she and Diana had the same sort of character.'

'What an extraordinary question. What did Granny say?'

'Said no, they were quite different.'

'Do you think Vicky knows what happened?'

'Shouldn't think so. She was only thirteen and it was all hushed up so quickly.'

'All the same, children are very knowing. Do you ever see anything of Dorothy?'

'Very little. She did bring Ralph to tea with Bruce the other afternoon but it wasn't a success. She's so bitter about everything. It made me feel quite unhappy.'

'I suppose it's understandable.'

'All the same, she shouldn't take it out on the King and her country. Makes everybody feel so uncomfortable. It needn't have turned her into a communist.'

'Maud, Clara — have you heard? Johnnie's been made a Director.'

'What — of that enormous Company? My goodness, he must be rich now. Perhaps he'll give us all presents!'

'Angus says he'll be worth thousands.'

'A weal tycoon! Do you wemember how he used to hand us all our pocket money?'

'Yes, Maud, and you always got the most.'

'Oh dear, did I? How nice for me!'

'John's very selfish. He'll never give us anything.'

'But he is good to Gwanny. I mean, giving her that lovely house in Oxford Woad to live in —'

'Someone told me they saw Dorothy marching along Kensington High Street wearing sandwich boards.'

'What on earth do you mean? Sandwich boards? Marching?'

'It was some sort of a demonstration. Spain, or something.'

'Spain? Marching? Over the Pywénées?'

'No, Maud, not *to* Spain, *for* Spain. There's some sort of a civil war on there.'

'Oh, what a pity. We wanted to go there for a holiday.'

'And someone else said they saw her at Marble Arch and she was waving her fists in the air.'

'*Poor* Bernard — and he's going to Buckingham Palace every Tuesday morning. He's doing busts of the King and Queen. I do hope it's not going to be bad for his weputation.'

So, month after month, the news buzzed round. The sisters did not care a fig for Mollie: she was a real Aunt Sally to be pelted with abuse. But they grieved about Dorothy, regretting very much that she was becoming increasingly remote from them, were sad that it seemed quite impossible to comfort her and were genuinely distressed that she was occupying herself in ways that seemed to them to be so eccentric.

The three sisters were not politically inclined. Their gifts were the inherited gifts of expressiveness — the co-ordination of eye, ear, imagination, hand. Rhetoric debate, oratory — these passed them by. They were not much interested in the movements of history, the pressures of international economics, except as these affected their own lives. Their minds were primarily practical; speculation seemed a waste of time. They had not got it in them to understand the fascination that ideas and policies could hold for a woman such as Dorothy. Domesticated to the core, the sisters would not have dreamed of trying to mould the future of the world.

'Do you know, Joyce, Annabella came to see us the other evening and the poor girl was really upset. Johnnie stayed away a whole week-end and she thinks he was with Mollie. Annabella was looking quite ill. She doesn't know what to do. I mean it's so difficult, being in a foreign country and all that.'

'He's impossible. Money's gone to his head.'

'Johnnie tells Salisbury he can't help it. He says that the women just won't leave him alone.'

'What can they see in him? He's not all that attractive.'

'Oh, I don't know, dear. He's got great appeal. I think the Italians would describe him as *furbo* and some women just can't resist that sort. And there's always the money!'

'If only he hadn't married Mollie in the first place. He might have had children. He'd have made such an affectionate father.'

'Annabella would love a family.'

'If *only* Mollie would give in about the divorce.'

'Yes. Never mind, I really rang up to tell you some good news. Betty's going to marry James. Isn't it splendid. He's such a nice, suitable young man.'

'He's the one she met while she was studying architecture, isn't he?'

'That's right. They say he's a very talented architect.'

'I *am* glad, dear. When?'

'Next year. I'm hoping Dorothy'll let Vicky be a bridesmaid and that she'll come herself. Then it'll be quite a family party again. They're going to Brazil for their honeymoon. He is a Brazilian.'

'All that way! How thrilling! Betty always did want a change from Clymping, didn't she!'

'Clara, isn't there anything we can do about Bernard and Dorothy? I mean, Weggie and I went to coffee there the other evening. There were several other visitors too. And Dorothy got all worked up about Spain and Abyssinia. She was so angwy that some of the guests said they'd never been so insulted in their life and they just walked out of the house. She said they were wicked and stupid because they didn't share her opinions.'

'How awful. What did Bernard do?'

'He just sat and bwooded. It was vewy embawwassing.'

'How dreadfully sad. Do you remember how lovely Dorothy used to be?'

'I shall never forget the way she looked at that dance when she and Bernard first met. She was weally wavishing. And so sweet.'

'And such fun. Do you remember the lovely way she

used to throw back her head and laugh. Oh dear, the things life does to people.'

'I think we must just not pay any attention to her. Let's just hope she'll grow out of all this. For Bernard's sake.'

The uninvolved are always worlds away from the uncomfortably passionate commitments of believers; to cool minds enthusiasm often appears crazy.

It was true that Dorothy did become almost impossible. She agitated and disturbed. She always had an answer. She was convinced that she was right. When she started to lay down the law, speaking with the fanatical authority of the newly-converted, about the corruption of the capitalist system and the new hope to be found in communism, a great many people who used to be her friends dropped her completely. And even the faithful, those who had known her in her careless girlhood, who loved her for her intrinsic goodness and charm, were often intolerably exasperated. They tried to excuse it on the grounds of Bernard's detachment as a husband, of the tragedy of Diana, but even so they found her fiercely-expressed opinions often rather tiresome.

But perhaps no one knew how much a part of her these new beliefs were, how they satisfied a real need in her being. No one knew the hours she spent working in the slums of the East End, sickened by the sight and the smell of poverty; no one knew how continuously she gave away a share of her small private income to help people in trouble. Probably only Vicky, who continued to receive her mother's strange confidences, realized how deeply she longed, during this period of her life, to devote herself to political causes, how she yearned to be at the barricades in Spain, stemming the advance of Fascism. She was torn between her desire to go out and fight for freedom and her fear of damaging Bernard in any way: her love for him always won, but it was a cruel inner struggle.

In the notebooks where Dorothy made scanty entries — comments on recent plays, rough drafts of letters to the papers, sketches of flowers for her embroidery, ideas for the poems she had recently started to write, quotations from political philosophers — she declared in her strong, gracious handwriting, 'I do not care that nobody likes me any longer.'

She was a wild, strange, proud one all right in those turbulent thirties, casting off the pain of Diana's death and of Bernard's silences, raging and agitating and dreaming of universal love and brotherhood, her face quivering and alight like some frail spirit of freedom. Too full of contradictions ever to be happy in an easy sort of way, she was, perhaps, at her best when she sat quietly by herself, hour after hour, forgetting clashes of class and sex as she composed her rich embroideries of fields and hedgerow, of English copses and Mediterranean hillsides.

It was a difficult home for children to grow up balanced and confident, burdened as it was with remorse and slit with disagreements; but it was endlessly interesting and alive.

To the studio door — which was really the front door — came models and artists, generals and admirals, came the rich and famous, came Granny, when she couldn't make herself heard at any other entrance. To the front door — which was really the back — came the workers, came lecturers from the London School of Economics, came Jewish refugees from Berlin, and weird little communists from Glasgow, came dedicated young men who had chosen to present their lives on 'that arid square, that fragment nipped off from hot Africa', who were off to join the International Brigade in Spain.

In the studio Bernard entertained his visitors with buns, small glasses of sherry, and wise, experienced talk about art and world history. Dorothy and her cronies drank water in the kitchen and talked of revolution.

Ralph was safely out of the way at boarding-school. Vicky was encouraged to join the Girl Guides. She sometimes wished her brother was home, too, to share the weight of these obsessed parents. She had no ally when they attacked each other across her, no support when her divided loyalties threatened to split her down the centre.

In the slap-dash journal Vicky sometimes resorted to at introspective moments during her harum-scarum schooldays she commented:

'It's terrible. The Italians have used gas on the Abyssinians. Mustard gas. Oh, I think I really will run away and go and fight in Spain. I want to get away from home anyway. It's so sad at home. And Mummy wouldn't mind if I went to help Spain.

'Mummy's always telling me how cruel Daddy is to her. How awful! I feel I'm older than she is and must try to protect her. But it's difficult because people often tell me I'm like Daddy. This makes me wonder if I'm cruel too. Am I a beastly person?

'Livia Gollings asked me to go marching with her on May Day. I don't really want to but perhaps I ought to. But I do hate it when Mummy makes me march for Arms for Spain and things like that.

'Daddy's doing a bust of me. I get sixpence an hour so I suppose it's not too bad.

'Today it was gorgeous 'cos I persuaded Heather to skip singing with me and we climbed out on to the school roof. It was marvellous. We watched the sunset and talked about love and marriage. She said I was terribly independent. Am I? I'm terribly lucky to have a friend like her.

'Mummy says I'll never get married. Well, I don't think I want to, so sucks. She says it would be nice if she and I could always live together. I don't want to, but I must try and be decent to her because of Diana and Daddy and everything.

'It was terribly funny in school today, because I organized the end of the world. When I banged on my desk everyone was to fall down dead. It happened in Scripture. Old Denny was standing there talking about Elijah and then suddenly I banged and we all fell down flat. It was a scream. She just stood there with her hair all frizzy, saying girls, girls, get up at once, get up.

'The King has died. That's a colossal piece of news and makes me feel I live in a very important time in history.

'How gorgeous, tomorrow we've got a netball match. Golly gollumptious, I adore netball.

'A sculptor called Eric Gill came to tea. He's a Roman Catholic and wears long black robes. I asked Daddy if he wore any trousers underneath and Daddy said he didn't know but if I asked Eric Gill he'd probably lift up his skirts and show me. Sometimes I think Daddy's awfully nice in spite of all Mummy says.

'Granny came to ask for some money. She's getting awfully short-sighted. When she goes to the cinema now she sits in the very front row and looks at the screen through field-glasses. I walked to the station with her and felt bored.

'I have a soul. I saw it, in the middle of prayers. It

was up in the air behind old Strud as she stood on the platform reading the lesson. It was white and it shone.

'This afternoon that funny Hungarian sculptor, Herr Strobl, leaned in through the dining-room window when I was doing my Latin prep and he told me all the different ways people in different countries kiss.

'I'm terribly bucked because I've been chosen to swim for the school. But I mustn't let myself grow into a swank.

'Daddy's gone for a cruise in the Mediterranean with his friend Commander Spooner on a battleship called H.M.S. *Repulse*. Mummy keeps a heavy ash stick by her bed in case anyone breaks in while he's away.

'Mummy and I and a communist went to see the grave of Karl Marx. It was very hot and the communist made a little paper hat and put it on her nose to stop it getting sunburned.

'I met a marvellous boy at the school dance and he asked me to have a cup of coffee with him on Saturday morning. Mummy said she'd have to come with me. I didn't go. Mummy says rich people are wicked. She says the working classes are the salt of the earth.

'I wish I was beautiful. I worship beauty. But everyone says I'm just like Daddy. And they say he's ugly. Oh well, never mind. I'll just have to try and make my soul beautiful.

'Mummy got charged by the mounted police at Hyde Park Corner. She said it was nasty. I do think Daddy might have been more sympathetic. He just grunted and went into the studio. I often think he's the wrong sort of husband for Mummy.

'I've been chosen to act in the school play. Sometimes I feel sure I have the fattest behind in the school. I'm sure no one wobbles as much as I do. I try and walk with my hands behind my back so's no one will see.

'I wonder if there really is going to be a war. Mummy and Daddy are always saying England's finished and it's an awful country. Is it? But when Mummy and I go out for country walks she's always saying what a beautiful country it is and how much she loves it and she stands by five-barred gates and sighs over the views. What *does* she mean? The other day we were cycling together and I swerved to avoid squashing a woolly caterpillar on the road and she said that when I'm grown-up and a famous revolutionary she'll tell everyone how much I cared about life and that I didn't even want to kill an insect. I don't want to be a revolutionary when I grow up. I'd much rather be a traveller. But I suppose that's terribly selfish when there're all these poor people in the world.

'I shall never forget. I met such a heavenly man to-day. He was quite old really, about twenty-three. He was a lorry driver and he gave me a lift to the top of the hill. Then he stopped the lorry and we just sat and talked and talked. He told me about the Docks and Limehouse and Soho and all the other places I'm longing to go to. He told me I'm going to be awfully attractive when I grow up and that I'll always have lots of men round me. Goodness, will I? I thought I was supposed to be ugly. I invited him to come home to supper and meet my parents. He said he'd better not. Why? I'm sure Mummy would approve 'cos he was working class. He said some girl had let him down badly and he hadn't got over it yet. He looked terribly sad. I know I'll never meet anyone like him again. Oh gosh, how bitter-sweet it was.

'Damn, blast and hell! It's the Royal Academy Private View tomorrow and I've got to go. I shall have to dress up and smile all the time. Worst of all everyone'll ask me what I want to be when I grow up and if I want to be an artist like everyone else in the family. And I'll feel awful because I don't know what I want to be. I wish I could explain that all I want is just to be a person and live —'

In spring, when every breath of soft air was an invitation to go out, even the sooty conglomerations of Kensington changed their aspect and became a gateway to adventure. And in prim and proper Putney Granny grew quite skittish as new life budded and bulged all round her in the garden.

The London season opened with a crush at the Private View at Burlington House. Everyone who was anybody went to that, to see and be seen; all the family managed to win or wheedle an invitation. It was a chance for a party, for face-to-face meetings and moments of truth. During the past four or five years family gatherings had, to Granny's sorrow, grown less frequent and less satisfying. She hoarded her memories of the times when she did manage to assemble some of the family — Betty's wedding, for instance (although Dorothy had refused to come to that), and Bruce's tenth birthday. There had been one exciting Guy Fawkes party, too, worth treasuring in her mind. The evening had been crisp with frost, the little boys had shrieked with joy as the jacks jumped and the catherine wheels twirled and the rockets hissed away up into the night, dropping their lovely stars with a soft crack. Ralph had dashed about the garden telling everyone that one day he would be going up there on a rocket to explore the Milky Way and he grew so excited that he was almost sick. Angus built a magnificent bonfire and Bruce and Jocelyn dragged out Apollo from the currant bushes and he was only saved from the flames in the nick of time — little rascals! And Granny had produced a lapful of chestnuts to roast in the embers and they had all stood around munching. She had heard that Bernard sometimes gave grand parties in his studio. But she was never invited. Only Reggie and Maud were, it seemed, smart enough to represent the family.

However, today she felt certain of seeing all her darlings at Burlington House. Somewhere there, in those lofty galleries, there would be a reunion; the family would converge upon her, as upon a still centre, from out of the noisy hurly-burly.

It was a very, very long way up the staircase into those galleries. Waiting at the bottom while Clara and Joyce dithered in the cloak-room she looked at the splendid flight of steps rising up in front of her and she felt quite faint. All that way — up and up and up — she could hardly see the misty summit where she knew the President would be waiting to receive her and to take her by the hand. She took off her glasses and polished them on her grey silk sleeve. Or would the President be there today? Did he receive guests at the Private View or at the Soirée when they were able to feast on deliciously tasty sandwiches and strawberries and cream? She couldn't remember, but decided she had better have her hand ready in case there was someone there to shake it.

'All right, dear? Ready?' Joyce bustled back, smiling.

'Do I look tidy? No hair sticking out?'

'You look very nice,' Clara assured her.

She had taken great trouble with her appearance. They said Bernard had a very fine piece of work on view this year and she didn't want to let him down. She wore a long dress made from a length of grey silk she had bought in the Christmas sales; it was cut low in front and had a fine piece of lace covering her throat. She had a jacket to match, white gloves and a large, black, artistic hat that she had adorned with two elegant grey feathers. Pinned on her jacket with a cameo brooch were three pink rosebuds plucked from the garden in the morning dew; round her neck hung a silver chain with a heavy locket dangling on her breast. Her face was flushed with excitement. She looked resplendent.

'Mind you don't tread on your dress as we go up,' warned Joyce. 'Perhaps you could just hold it up a little.'

'And when you meet the President don't forget to shake hands,' said Clara.

This President who might or might not be standing there at the top of the stairs — he did present a problem. Her memory for names was not as good as it had been and she could not recollect who it was this year. Was it that quaint man Bernard had once introduced her to, Sir Edwin Lutyens? Or was it — ? Who was it? She grasped the rail and slowly started to climb — one step, two steps, three steps — moving with pride and trying to hold her head high. How quickly time had gone! It seemed only a few years ago that she had almost danced up these stairs on the arm of her husband, Philip, who was exhibiting a head and shoulders portrait bust of her. 'A Young Mother' he had called it and everyone had crowded round to praise him. But had time really flown so fast? No, indeed no, it was an age since she had last seen him, so many years alone without him. Suppose he was suddenly to appear, standing on the next step looking down at her — strong beard, laughing eyes and all — supposing — Oh, she would faint with joy.

'I'll just have a little rest on this step, Clara,' she

said, and she laid her right hand on her heart to still its wild, girlish beating.

'Are you all right, dear?' asked Joyce.

'I just had a little turn. A silly fancy. I'll be all right in a minute.'

The President — that name on the tip of her tongue — Sir Somebody Somebody. Ah, she had it. Of course, it was Sir Joshua Reynolds. Clutching this fact in her mind, she climbed bravely on. Light from the galleries above streamed down on her, gay young people in bright clothes flashed up past her, like Mercury. But at last she was there, at the final step, holding out her hand to the uniformed attendant collecting the invitation cards, smiling and murmuring 'Delighted, Sir Joshua, delighted. I expect you know my son, Bernard.'

And the courteous attendant gave an imperceptible little tug and uttered some appropriate phrase and she was safe at the top. She passed on through into the first gallery, mingled with the fashionable crowd, bowed ceremoniously at anyone who looked her way, peered at paintings and said to her daughters: 'Isn't everybody kind. Isn't it all nice. I love parties. There's only one thing wrong at this party. There's nothing to eat. Let's see if we can find Bernard. I'm sure he'll take us out to lunch later on. I was so busy getting dressed up I didn't have time for much breakfast.'

'Rather like looking for the proverbial needle,' retorted Clara, who suspected that Bernard dodged away whenever he saw Granny approaching.

'If we go towards the sculpture hall and just sit there everyone'll be sure to find us. I said to everyone — *sculpture.*'

Flanked by her daughters, her rear protected by gallant Angus and Salisbury, she pushed along, willing the rest of the family to be drawn towards her. She was particularly looking forward to seeing Annabella again. John hadn't brought her for Sunday tea at Oxford Road for several weeks.

People, people — dressed up to the nines, coming and going, milling around her, approaching, bowing, smiling, passing on — you could hardly see the pictures for the people — and now and again someone detaching himself from the multitude and taking shape as Reggie, who seemed to have grown in stature since becoming Principal of the Royal College of Art, as darling Uncle Merrie smaller than ever and frail as a waif but just as affectionate and covering her hands with kisses in the old familiar way, as her nephew Cedric, rosy as a farmer and thrilled because he had discovered a bishop perched on a respectable branch of the family tree that now peeped over the top of his pocket ready to be shown to anyone who was interested.

'Look!' said Salisbury, 'There's Augustus John! Doesn't he look every inch an artist? And hasn't he got a jolly, pink nose?'

'Good heavens,' said Angus. 'Blowed if that isn't Jack Hobbs! Great man!'

But Granny didn't have time to look because a man whom age was beginning to bend double appeared in front of her and, sweeping off his top hat, said, 'My dear lady, I saw you once in a bus and I never forgot you. I had never seen such a wonderful complexion.' He put on his hat again and tottered away.

'Who was that?' asked Clara.

'Someone I met in a bus,' replied Granny in perplexity. 'Oh dear, what a crowd! Isn't it hot!' She began to wave a handkerchief about in front of her face. 'I would like a glass of water. Where do you think Bernard's got to?'

Bernard, gaily circulating as though at a private

party, was aware that Granny was stalking him like some well-intentioned Fury; he observed the family out of the corner of his pince-nez and gave them the slip for as long as possible.

Then, suddenly, they all converged, as Granny had foreseen, in the sculpture hall. Bernard's work, his 'Eternal Meeting', an over-lifesize figure of a man and woman embracing, had pride of place in the centre.

'Sold it yet, dear boy?' asked Reggie.

'Give him a chance,' smiled Maud. 'It's only been on view an hour or two.'

'As a matter of fact,' said Bernard, 'I have had enquiries already. A charming American woman thinks she'd like to put it in her park near Guildford. She wants to know if she could pay by instalments — a refined sort of hire-purchase.'

'I am so proud of you,' murmured Granny. 'You know it doesn't seem all that long ago I was taking you to have tea in Alfred Gilbert's studio. You were just a little fellow in knickerbockers.'

'Yes, Mother, yes.' Bernard looked about him for a place where he could hide, if necessary.

'And he was advising me to put you in for sculpture.'

'No, Mother, he didn't,' contradicted Bernard. 'I have a very good memory, you know, and I can recall the occasion clearly. We ate iced biscuits and he said that whatever you did with me you shouldn't let me take up sculpture. He said it was a dreadful life.'

'Did he really say that? Oh dear, what a nuisance.'

'Never mind. I don't regret it. Not any longer. I've come to terms with the dreadfulness, Mother. And if I didn't get such bad chilblains in the winter I might almost positively enjoy my sculptor's life.'

'We were sorry you couldn't manage to come to Betty's wedding,' said Clara to Dorothy, who was dressed all in beige and looked rather subdued. 'It would have been nice to have Vicky as a bridesmaid.'

Dorothy smiled and said something inaudible.

'It's nice and cool in here,' said Granny. 'Ever so nice and empty.'

'Yes, sculpture always gets the least attention,' remarked Bernard ruefully. 'But, you know, it's the most permanent of all the arts. Sculpture survives all kinds of catastrophes and cataclysms. It's buried for centuries under the lava from volcanic eruptions, it's lost for hundreds of years and then found again smothered by the jungle, it's dredged up from the bottom of the sea in a fisherman's net —'

'I don't know what people of the future'll say when they excavate some of the figures that are starting to creep into modern exhibitions now,' commented Salisbury. 'Spiky, blobby creatures, elongated, battered — they can't be understood with the eye — they need critics to write about them first — Future generations will say we were all mad!'

'And perhaps they'll be right. The sculpture you speak of is the *avant-garde* of decadence.'

'Oh, I don't know,' remonstrated Reggie. 'That's putting it a bit too strongly.' As Principal of the most important art college in the country his position was delicate and he did not feel able to dismiss entirely the new trends in art. 'People must have their jokes now and then.'

'If only they would take it as a joke,' said Bernard. 'But the artists themselves take it all so seriously. They've got no humility. It was just the same when Rome was dying. There were the most monstrous, contorted, ludicrous forms of art. It's as though the psyche disintegrates as the power of the tribe wanes. An inseparable partnership. Now, Spengler says that —

'How's Ralph, dear?' asked Joyce.

'Rather spotty,' replied Dorothy.

'Try a little Vaseline,' suggested Granny.

'His sort of spots need something stronger than that. Boys don't wash much at boarding-school. But he's very cheerful. Bernard and I went down to see him last Sunday. He ate a good tea and seemed to be enjoying himself.'

'How about you, Vicky love? Have you decided what you're going to do when you leave school?'

Vicky shook her head and smiled foolishly. Actually she was thinking just then of Ralph's last letter to her:

'I say, old thing, do try and stop the parents coming down to see me. All the other chaps' parents come by car. Mine come by Green Line coach. I feel such an ass. They take me out for a walk along country lanes and all the other chaps whizz past in cars and make faces at me. I don't half get teased about it afterwards. I always have to walk in the middle, a parent on each side. And Daddy's hat is always so *large*. Try and *do* something.'

'What's the Tate done with the figure of yours it bought last year?' asked Reggie. 'I haven't seen it on view.'

'It's locked up in their cellars. It's not modern enough.'

'Its day'll come, Bernard,' comforted Reggie.

'You know, Reggie, old chap, I'm not mentioning any names, but there are people with a very curious sort of mentality gaining great power and influence in the art world today.'

'Well, er —' Reggie knew what he meant but could not afford to say so.

'Yes, there's an unpleasant streak of perversity. It's going to have a bad influence. Did you know, by the way, that we have a priceless piece of sculpture here, in Burlington House?'

'Well —'

'I'll take you along to see it one day. It's a little carving by Michelangelo. Beyond price! Beautiful! Somerset Maugham was here as a guest at one of our banquets and do you know he wept when he saw this carving. It moved him so much.'

'Bernard —' Granny felt something important was missing and she suddenly remembered what it was. 'You did send Johnnie an invitation, didn't you?'

'Yes, Mother, I did as you asked.'

'Do you know what John gave Betty for a wedding present,' said Clara. 'He gave her a vacuum cleaner. But I bet it didn't cost him much because he got it through his Company!'

'Wemember those pwesents fwom Wussia?' smiled Maud.

Bernard winced. Surely they weren't going to start their gossiping here. He looked wildly left and right for help.

'I mean, with all those thousands. Don't you think he should give more to his family, Dorothy? To his nieces and nephews?' Clara appealed to John's sworn adversary.

Dorothy rubbed her forehead and considered.

Bernard caught sight of a woman he knew circling slowly round his *bianco del mare* marble lovers. She smiled at him and he began to edge away from the family.

'No, I don't think he should,' disagreed Dorothy, for once on John's side. 'I really don't think so. Why should he? He had a man's responsibilities when he was still a schoolboy. He looked after all of you when he was very young. Perhaps he did more than was good for him. I mean, perhaps his resilience was over-taxed. You can't expect him to go on doing it all his life.'

'Where's Bernard gone?' Granny always felt nervous when Dorothy made pronouncements in a voice that brooked no denial. 'I can't see him any longer.'

'Bernard's very attractive to women,' Clara reminded her, as though that answered the question.

'But Bernard, dear,' came the laughing voice of an unknown woman from the other side of the statue, 'you've called it "Eternal Meeting". Why *eternal*?'

'My dear,' came Bernard's deep, measured voice. 'Need you ask? Just *look*. How does that poem go — "All night through the torches burn, Lip to lip and thigh to thigh, And the rest is silence" — or something like that.'

'I don't think,' remarked Dorothy tartly, 'that Bernard had his eternal meeting with me.' She stretched a smile across her face.

'Of course he did, dear,' said Joyce, quick to comfort.

'Oh, there's Sawah,' said Maud. 'Sa — wah —'

Sarah appeared squired by three or four young men. She had grown rather thin lately and looked interesting as well as alluring. She kissed Granny, smiled all round, said she simply couldn't stop as she'd promised to go and look at the portrait someone had painted of her and glided away with her escorts.

'I do wish she'd huwwy up and get mawwied,' complained Maud. 'It's time she did settle down. She's older than Betty.'

'I wonder where Johnnie is,' said Granny. She was beginning to feel tired now and her voice was plaintive. 'Johnnie!' With a sigh she sat herself down on a couch.

Bernard and the unknown lady had disappeared, Dorothy and Vicky were trailing away into another gallery and Reggie and Maud were starting to say 'Well, I suppose we'd better move on. You must all come to a meal with us soon.'

Those who were left said they'd love to, although they knew very well that these vague invitations were never followed up.

'I thought Bernard might take us to have some lunch,' said Granny.

'Rather a lot of us,' said Joyce.

'I've got lots of ham and salad at home,' said Clara, seeing where her duty lay. 'And bottled fruit from Clymping. You'd all better come back with us.'

'Perhaps we'll see Johnnie as we go.' Grannie adjusted her hat and breathed on her glasses again. 'I do so want to see Annabella again soon. I do enjoy it when she comes to tea with me. She's so refined. And such a pretty voice.'

John loomed up at them in Gallery Three. They could not miss him. He was standing in the middle looking all about him with clever, observant eyes. His clothes had the look of coming from the very best tailors; his face glowed with self-satisfaction.

'Mother — darling —' he roared across the gallery and held out his arms. He was never backward in expressing his affection for her and she loved him for this demonstrativeness.

'Who's that with him, by his side? Joyce? Clara? Who is it? That's not Annabella. Annabella's not stout. Oh dear, I really must go and see the occulist again and get some stronger glasses.'

'Hush, Mother, hush,' begged her daughters, who saw only too well who the woman by Johnnie's side was. 'We mustn't have a scene here. Just behave as though everything's quite normal.'

'*Mütterlein! Liebling!*' John flung his arms round

her, kissing her loudly on both cheeks. '*Du bist immer das schönste Weib.*'

A step behind Johnnie stood Mollie, Mollie smiling and saying 'Hullo, how are you?' to her sisters-in-law as though nothing had happened, Mollie with diamond-and-sapphire earrings in her rosy little ears, Mollie just touching the bottom of John's jacket with her fingers as though she couldn't bear to let him stir an inch from her side.

'Hullo, Mother,' she said, when John released Granny enough to allow her to peep round his bulky shoulder. 'Busy here today, isn't it?'

'Johnnie?' Granny looked imploringly at her first-born.

'That's a lovely hat you're wearing, sweetheart,' he replied. 'You don't look a day over thirty-five. Mollie and I were just thinking about a spot of lunch. How about it?'

His glance did not include his sisters and brothers-in-law. He had eyes only for Granny and, in spite of his warm greeting, those shrewd eyes did not look as though it would matter very much if she refused his invitation.

'She's coming home with us,' put in Clara quickly, afraid of what might happen. 'It's all arranged. We're on our way now.'

'See you on Sunday, then. Why not come and have tea,' said Mollie cosily, as though this had been a regular thing for years.

Granny stood shaking her head, moving her lips dumbly. She felt stunned and she allowed her daughters to pilot her away, down the great staircase, out of Burlington House, past the statue of Sir Joshua Reynolds and into the car Salisbury had waiting.

Only when they reached Clara's home could she

bring herself to speak. '*Busy here today!* What a thing to say! She made the Royal Academy sound like a common bazaar.'

Later that day the sisters' telephones were ringing upstairs and down and words of astonishment were speeding along the secret lines of communication.

'Whatever's happened to Annabella?'

'Has Mollie got him back for good?'

'You'd think he would have warned us.'

'Poor Granny, it put her right off her lunch.'

'The way Mollie just stood there. She looked so smug.'

'I've been trying to ring Annabella's flat. But the operator can't get any answer. He says the line's been disconnected.'

'John's dweadful. He shouldn't do these things.'

Indignant expostulations, ineffectual protests, questions that would never be given a straight answer. John was always very adroit at avoiding unpleasant explanations: and the sisters anyway soon concluded that it was really none of their business and they might as well wash their hands of John and his love-affairs that had always been a source of worry and embarrassment to them.

CHAPTER NINE

JOHN was very wealthy now. His home in the *nouveau-riche* suburb of Kingston wanted for nothing. He spent money freely on his comforts; so did Mollie, making the most of it after those years of gnawing misery. They amassed and hoarded, they wrapped themselves up in their possessions, even having double layers of Persian carpets on the floors rather than give any away. John's firm provided him with a Daimler and with a chauffeur who opened doors and touched his cap and on cold days tucked a fur rug round his master's knees.

John must by now have been aware that war was inevitable; the powerful set of international business men among whom he moved could not fail to observe signs and portents as they daily worried about how to safeguard their fortunes. The Nazis were increasingly degrading Central Europe into a ghastly parody of an insect state. Escape routes to the sea were crowded with Jews and others scrambling to get away before it was too late. Every day in Berlin, in Frankfurt, Vienna, Leipzig and all the main-line stations agonized parents were managing to bundle their children away in trains and then return home alone to face the lengthening shadow of the gas ovens. And, in two or three years another enemy besides the war, a hidden, personal enemy, was to strike at John.

However, in happy ignorance of future illness and snapping their fingers at the approaching spectre of goose-stepping madmen, Johnnie and Mollie set out to have a prolonged binge. There were shopping sprees in and out of the art dealers and the chic boutiques round about St. James's Street and Park Lane. There were dinners at the Ritz and lunches at the Dorchester. They took Granny out to tea at Lyons' Corner House, where she ate vast quantities of buttered scones and honey as the musicians fiddled away under the palms. There were trips to Paris and Berlin, Geneva, Zürich, Rome, with rooms at the best hotels, oysters every evening, rare steaks and miraculous syllabubs. At appropriate seasons salmon was delivered from the waterfalls of Scotland, grouse from the Yorkshire moors; the best pork pies came specially from Nottingham and Fortnum and Mason could provide fresh raspberries and strawberries any time he wanted them. Harrods delivered shrimps every day.

Possibly it was a vision of such a life, flowing with food and money, that had sustained John in Chelsea when the fare was plain, when he rose early every morning to practise his music and worried late into the night because his mother wasn't able to manage her housekeeping money properly.

Granny often went to concerts with them and for drives into the country. On these occasions she sat in the back with Johnnie, sharing his fur rug. She enjoyed every moment of this high living and she had grown too wise, now, and was, basically, too flexible to go on nursing her grudges against Mollie for ever. The two women made a sort of peace. Johnnie called Mollie 'the old girl' and was never seen to kiss her; she referred to him as 'my young man' and waited on him hand and foot. Now and then they visited the rest of the family and very occasionally one or other of them would be allowed to slide in through the front door at Kingston and get a glimpse of the opulence within.

'My dear — have you *seen* the Persian rugs!'

'Mollie says that whatever takes her fancy she buys.'

'I should think she must cost John a pretty penny in brandy. Did you see all those empties?'

'Why did he go back to her? *Why*?'

No one ever discovered why. Had Johnnie been overcome by guilt at a moment of personal crisis? Did he wake in the night troubled by indigestion and approaching old age? Was Mollie's cooking irresistible? Did the gentle Annabella decide finally that she could bear the ambiguities of her position no longer, that her youth was passing away and that the way things were going she would never settle down with a lawful husband and the respect of society? Perhaps she received disquieting news from Vienna, news of brutal men, of neighbours disappearing for ever in the night, and wanted to be reunited with her people before darkness fell. Or it may simply have been that Mollie's persistent love, urgent as some primordial power, won the day. For a while the family went on fretting over these undisclosed reasons. Then time washed over the affair and the hopes and fears of the thirties went jazzing along towards the day of reckoning.

One day Mollie telephoned Vicky and said: 'So you've left school, darlin'. I hear you're going abroad.'

'Yes. Next month, actually.'

'Would you like to come to tea with me tomorrow afternoon?'

'I'd love to.'

'Your mother's always been very good to me. I want to give you a present before you go.'

February was mild that year. The almond trees were already in blossom; the rather unhealthy pink of their flowers had a greenish tinge in the amethyst-coloured air of late afternoon.

'You should see them in Japan,' said Mollie, opening the door to her visitor. 'And the peach trees.'

'You've been to Japan?' Vicky was a glutton for travellers' tales.

'Oh yes. Your uncle and I went there years ago on business. They're very clean, dainty people, the Japanese. I loved it there. Well, take off your coat, darlin'. We'll have tea directly. The kettle's humming. You don't mind Earl Grey, do you? My young man'll drink only the best.'

Near the window stood a small, round table laid with tea things. The lawns outside were splashed with purple and yellow crocuses; the gardener could be seen stooping lovingly over the rose bushes. Mollie carried in a silver teapot that reflected the firelight. With a yawn she sank back into a deep arm-chair and motioned to her visitor to do likewise. They sat and smiled at each other. Vicky, who had been kept in ignorance of the ups and down of Mollie's life, always felt easy with this aunt. It seemed to her that a warm kindliness flowed out from the stout, silver-haired woman and she felt she would be able to talk to her about all those worrying problems at home, talk without reserve — if only Mollie would start her off with the right sort of question.

'So you're going abroad?' said Mollie. 'What made you decide to do that?'

Not the sort of question she wanted. In fact she

didn't know how to answer it because her reasons for going were too tangled up for sensible words. Luckily Mollie was merely being conversational and quickly passed on to the next question.

'What'll you do abroad, darlin'?'

That was easier. 'Study languages.'

'Good idea. Now then, sweetheart, help yourself to something to eat. Do you take milk in your tea? Sugar? There's a little jar of *patum paperium* there. Your uncle loves his gentleman's relish.'

The cups were frail as egg shells and almost transparent. The table cloth was snowy white and edged with a deep border of fine, rare lace. Everything told of good taste and a bulging purse. Vicky ate thin slices of bread and butter and wondered what her present would be. She felt sure it would be something glamorous and exotic.

'So you're going to study languages. To get a good job with when you come home, I suppose?'

'I suppose so.'

'What will you do?'

'When I come home? Well — er — I had thought of acting.'

'Acting? Hm — I don't know — Well, at least you've got your father's speaking voice and that should be an asset. Have you heard your cousin Betty's expecting a baby? And Deborah's doing ever so well at the Architectural Association. They're both very sensible girls. Do you often see them?'

'No.'

The inquisition continued, that question-and-answer conversation that feels for common ground. Now and then a mahogany grandfather clock told the time in a voice as pure as a choir boy's.

'And is your mother still a communist?'

'I think she's something called a trotskyist now. Something to do with the fourth international — or something.'

'Trotsky! Him! Trotsky's the worst of the lot. Even worse than that Lenin. I once saw old Trotters and I thought he looked just like the devil. You don't want to believe all your mother says, Vickers. She doesn't always know what she's saying. Your father's not always very kind to her. They're very difficult to live with, those two young men of ours! But you see, Vicky, your mother wasn't *there*. You know your uncle was British Consul in Moscow during the revolution, don't you?'

Vicky hadn't known. It sounded incredible.

'Your mother, bless her, didn't see those mobs with their shaggy hair and their rags. And all that blood. The swords and the revolvers. It wasn't very pretty. We had to run for our lives. Across the frozen rivers — the Volga, the Dnieper, the Neva — all of them. Those communists were like wolves. A bloodthirsty pack!'

Vicky thought of the polite men and women, sober as Quakers, who now and then sat at the scrubbed kitchen table and talked about bathrooms for everyone and better schools. She felt she should interrupt and try to explain her mother's point of view, but when Mollie and Johnnie got excited about the Bolsheviks their voices roared like rivers in spate and it was as useless to try and curb them as it was to quench her mother's fiery prophecies. She sighed and wondered whether she would ever be able to reconcile these raging people.

'And your brother? How's Ralph?'

This was better. Her brother was easy. She loved and understood him. He was well, thank you.

'He's an interesting boy. Always passionate about something, isn't he, always absorbed? Once it was tigers. And bridges. And engines. And China. I remember

175

how he used to dress up in Chinese clothes and plan campaigns.'

'I think it's the stars now. He's always talking about Mars and Saturn and places and how to get there.'

'Your uncle's got lots of books about the universe. He's very interested in the heavens. He may have got one or two old ones he doesn't want any longer. I'll have to ask him. He's very fond of all his nieces and nephews. Very fond indeed.'

Outside the window the February evening was the colour of ink. Tangled up in the spiky twigs of a peach tree Venus shone with a green light. The fire in the grate was a fading sun.

'It's getting dark,' said Mollie.

She touched a switch and a crystal chandelier sprang to life, glittering like a shower of meteors.

'Look, isn't it lovely!' Mollie gazed up. 'Like diamonds. When I'm by myself I often turn it on and off. Just for the pleasure of seeing it sparkle. I saw it in a shop window in Knightsbridge and I went straight in and bought it. And I liked it so much that I went back and bought two more exactly the same. Hurry up and finish your tea, darlin'. I want to show you round the house.'

With the pride of a newly-married woman she conducted her seventeen-year-old niece on a sightseeing tour. She pulled open drawers to display her beloved linen, lifted the lids of chests to show blankets and quilts, flung open cupboard doors and pointed to shelves of exquisite goblets that chimed like distant bells when she struck them with her polished finger nail; she even counted out the sheets in the airing cupboard, finest Irish linen all of them. Vicky exhausted her stock of admiring exclamations and took to saying 'Oh! Oh!' There was silver to be praised, wedgwood vases,

oriental ivories, Staffordshire figurines, French porce-
lain, Russian ikons — to say nothing of those Persian
rugs laid so thickly over the floors, one or two even
hanging from the walls. There were wardrobes filled
with silk dresses and fur coats. There were intriguing
little wooden cabinets that smelt of joss sticks. It was
all rather heady, especially to someone expecting to
receive a gift.

'Like it?' asked Mollie, when the expedition at last
finished up in the kitchen where all the gadgets were
the very latest thing, where the shelves were stocked
with food.

'Lovely.'

'And what would you like —'

The difficulty was going to be to choose what.

'— to do now?'

'Oh — er — Vicky twisted her hands behind her
back. 'Would you like me to do the washing-up? I'll
have to go soon, actually. I — er — promised Mummy
I wouldn't be late.' Perhaps a little tactful pressure
would hurry her up.

'We'll do the washing-up together, sweetheart. Then
we'll sit down and have another little chat before you go.'

Had Mollie forgotten? Could it have been a joke?

They whisked through the washing-up and then
drew their chairs close to the fire and resumed their
question-and-answer talk.

'Is your mother still doing her lovely embroidery?'

'Yes. Someone bought one the other day.'

'My word, what a family you are! Always doing
something. And what about your father? Working like
a nigger, I expect. They'll probably make him a knight
one of these days.'

'Sir Bernard — I don't think Mummy'd like that
very much.'

'Nonsense, she'd love it! She's as Tory as I am at heart. A real old aristocrat!'

'Well — I'd better be going now.' There was no point in prolonging frustrated anticipation.

'Must you? Oh, by the way, there's something I wanted to show you. You like books, don't you?'

'Yes. Though actually I've got quite a lot already.'

'Have you?' Mollie looked puzzled. 'Anyway, just tell me what you think of these.'

She pattered away on her high little heels, returning with something done up in snowy tissue paper. 'I saw them the other day. In a little place off Bond Street. And I thought — look —'

'Yes, oh yes —' They were very lovely, two jade ornaments twisting and curving like frozen green flames, mounted on bases of carved ebony.

'— and I thought they'd make beautiful book-ends. What do you think?'

'May I?' Vicky stretched out her hands and took them. They were cool, and heavy as river water. She laid them against her cheek and closed her eyes. What beauties! Just right for her growing collection of poetry books.

'Yes, they are lovely, aren't they,' agreed Mollie. 'I felt sure you'd appreciate them. With all your artistic upbringing. The moment I saw them I knew they'd be just right for my young man. They can prop up all his books about Chinese art. Keep them tidy.'

'I shall have to go now. Really.' Vicky relinquished the treasures and pushed herself up from the chair.

'I suppose you'd better, me darlin'. It's been nice having you. I'm always so interested in your family. In those days when I didn't know where to turn I could always rely on your mother. We used to go for walks together.'

'I'm glad.'

'And you have a good time abroad. When you work
— work. And when you play — you jolly well play.
And send us a picture postcard. My young man and I
go abroad a lot so we might call and see you in Switzer-
land. Take you out to have a meringue glacé!'

'That'd be lovely.' Vicky put on her coat, tossed
back her hair, leaned forward to be kissed.

'Wait a minute, pet. Isn't it a silly I am. Forgetting
all about the present I want to give you. Come back in
the warm sitting-room. It's under the sofa.'

Mollie went down on her hands and knees, groping
about on the floor.

'This is what I want you to have,' she said, pulling
out something soft, done up in blue paper. She gave
herself a quaint little shake, like a hen that has just
laid an egg, and handed the parcel to her niece. 'As a
keepsake, darlin'. When you were a little girl you came
out with your mother and me for one of our walks. It
was winter and she and I were talking away so much we
forgot all about you. And when we looked round we
saw you were crying with the cold. Your poor little
hands were all icy. I've been meaning to give you this
for a long time.'

It was a muff — a huge, ermine muff, yellow with
age and smelling of mothballs.

Vicky stared at it. Was she to hang it on her wall,
like a holiday memento? Was she to use it in bed to
keep her feet warm? Suddenly she saw herself walking
down Regent Street in a sleek black coat with her hands
folded primly inside this decrepit piece of fur and she
burst out laughing.

'What's the matter? Don't you like it?' Mollie spoke
sharply, like an insulted shopkeeper. 'It's a good piece.
Came from Russia.'

Vicky was searching for words with which to express her feelings when the dignified grandfather sang out six o'clock in his astonishing treble voice.

'Goodness, my young man'll be home any minute,' said Mollie. 'You'd better be off now, Vickers.'

With the muff wrapped in its blue paper under her arm Vicky walked towards the train that would take her home — that rather austere, sparse home where her parents genuinely preferred to live on the minimum, avoiding clutter and paring their possessions down to the essential. She tossed Mollie's keepsake into her bedroom cupboard where it stayed in the darkness for many years.

Granny said she was glad Vicky was going abroad. It was a sensible thing to do. She had always encouraged her children to *go* and to *do*. Some people, she said, without mentioning any names, made a great cry about poverty and yes, it was certainly a very sad thing to be without enough money and have to scrape and screw. All her children, she said, had had very little money when they were young and she herself had had to try and remember to count every ha'penny. But lack of money, she said, didn't stop people enjoying themselves. Her children — look at all the things they'd done, all the fun they'd had. They had all gone to Germany. Bernard had worked his passage to America, Clara had gone to Italy on the wings of music, Joyce had motor-cycled round France, Johnnie had gone everywhere. It was work that mattered, Granny said, and using your head, and not being afraid.

'Bless you, love,' she said, 'You make the most of it.'

She edged six handkerchiefs with lace from Woolworths, embroidered a V on each one and said, 'Please write to me. I can't get about as easily as I used to.

Sometimes, you know, I start to run for a bus. And it's nasty — I find I can't run.'

Granny fought against her increasing age valiantly, but the more she battled the more viciously did her adversary sneak back, pinching, twisting, tripping her up. She began more and more to feel the burden of her body. Most of her light-footed active life she had worn it like a comfortable dress; it had fitted her perfectly and she had hardly felt it. But now pain began to engrave its outlines and its parts. Rheumatism painted her arms and legs with flames. The skeleton began to obtrude through her skin, like an emerging statue. Her hair was still brown, her teeth her own, her famous complexion still soft and clear. But her eyes did not play fair with her; they led her to bruise her sides against corners, to mistake her steps and tumble down the stairs. Doctors no longer paid much attention to her plaintive murmurs, so she turned to unorthodox methods of healing and comfort.

Except for some distant cousins who lived in the basement — silent, frightened women who flitted about the house and garden like moths — Granny was once more alone at Oxford Road. The rooms were dustier and stuffier than of old and the garden was growing unkempt. Armies of sunflowers and michaelmas daisies marched all over it, fighting back the softer tribes of delphiniums and poppies, waving their brilliant banners of victory in the late summer. The honeysuckle over the back porch stuck out in all directions like an untidy head of hair. The currants from Moscow down in the far corner had long ago outgrown their strength and were being choked by tough little elder bushes. The plaster casts of grandfather's work had melted away in the wind and rain.

All about the place, however, there was always a

wonderfully sweet smell — sweet briar and lavender, lime, jasmine, lilac. Granny spent much time wandering around, rubbing aromatic leaves in her fingers, sniffing at her hands, falling into reveries. Sometimes she would suddenly leave off whatever she happened to be doing and sit down at the piano fumbling out some old melody with her stiff fingers — and then again fall to dreaming.

The family didn't like her to be left alone too much. They tried to see to it that someone went to keep her company as often as possible. The grandchildren were good-tempered and took it in turns to visit her. Granny loved them all equally, but possibly her favourite companion during these fading years was the peaceful Deborah. Betty was now taken up with her new baby, Sarah was always off to grand places, Vicky was restless and she couldn't really expect the boys to sit still and talk to her. Deborah was so nice and quiet and affectionate and she never seemed to mind spending the afternoon with her.

Dependent without being clinging, Deborah lived well within the limits of her strength. She was loving, loyal, dutiful and well-balanced. Indifferent health inclined her to be languid, although in any sedentary occupation she could be energetic. She had inherited her father's hands, those mobile hands of Salisbury with the broad, bent-back sculptor's thumb, and could make anything she wanted to. She was particularly adept at sewing and this won Granny's praise and approval, for she, too, in the old days, had liked nothing better than to busy herself with yards of lovely material, draping and cutting and fashioning it into something delightful and original. Now, at twenty and looking very much younger, Deborah was opening out into a diffident prettiness. Her features, though unremarkable, were pleasant, her expression sweet, her voice gentle, her hair long and silky. She was beginning to fall in love with a fellow student at the Architectural Association and emotion lent her a mild allure.

'Shall I read to you, Granny. It'd rest your eyes.'

'I'd love a bit from the Bible. Do you think you could? It's over there. On the piano.'

'Anything special you'd like?'

'Just something nice and kind from the New Testament. Perhaps that bit where Jesus says about the suffering being blessed. I never get tired of that bit. It's so comforting. Do you think you could find it, love?'

Deborah found her way to Matthew, Chapter Five. 'Blessed are the poor in spirit — is that the bit you want?'

'That sounds nice. But wait a bit while I get my sewing. Never do to sit with idle hands, would it?'

'But can you see, Granny? Enough to sew, I mean. Shall I do it for you?'

'My eyes are all right for making lavender bags. I picked the lavender from the bushes in the back garden. And dried it in the oven. I thought little bags'd make nice Christmas presents for all of you. To slip in among your underclothes and keep them sweet-smelling.'

'Blessed are they that mourn,' went on Deborah, 'for they shall be comforted. Blessed are the meek, for they shall inherit the earth. Blessed are they which —'

'I go to church a lot now, you know. I miss it when I don't go. All that singing's lovely. And it's nice and warm. Last Sunday I had people coming to lunch and I badly wanted to go to church as well. But I had to leave it in God's hands. I did lots of jobs while I was eating my breakfast. I always do things while I have breakfast, you know. And then I scrubbed the potatoes and did the beans and I put the two tables together and laid a cloth over both of them. And after all that there was still time to go to church. But I had a terrible attack of neuralgia during the sermon. Oh, it *was* bad.'

'Poor Granny, I'm so sorry.'

'Never mind. You know they say in my Christian Science Handbook that the only substance is spirit and that all sickness is a delusion. Fancy that!'

'Fancy!'

'And that everyone's good in God's eyes. Does that mean this Hitler person? I have quite a puzzle thinking it all out.'

'I'm sure you do.'

'Bruce plays the piano so beautifully now. And sing! Oh, how he sings! He's got into a choir school, you know.'

'Has he?' Deborah shut the Bible. Granny really preferred talking to being read to. Deborah didn't mind. She had rather a backache and was content to sit back and dream of the dark-haired boy with the saturnine face who asked her to have coffee with him every day now, letting Granny's reminiscences impinge on her consciousness now and then. She had heard all the stories before, but they didn't bore her. Those she liked best were the Christmas ones — Uncle Merrie dressed up as a Crusader and all the other uncles clad in bath towels and waving wooden swords, Uncle Merrie dressed up as a Columbine, Uncle Merrie dressed up as the Lady Mayoress of Fulham and stand-on his head —

'Daddy's making a marvellous present for Betty's baby,' she told Granny. 'He says he'll have it done by Christmas.'

'What is it?'

'He's keeping it a secret. You know what he's like!'

Yes, Granny knew her Salisbury — there was nobody like him for presents and surprises. She felt happy thinking of him at work on his secret gift; Salisbury was almost as dear to her as her own children.

'He's collecting all the old watches he can lay hands on,' said Deborah, 'so I suppose it'll be something clockwork.'

'I wonder what.'

'So do I.'

'I do so hope we'll have a nice Christmas party this year. It's been ever such a long time since we had a proper Christmas at Oxford Road. It used to be so nice when you were all little. Did I ever tell you about the Christmas when I caught a turkey?'

'The time you were out shopping in a hurry?' Deborah had heard the story many times but never minded it being repeated. It was so funny and so typical of Granny.

'That's right. I was rushing round on Christmas Eve, getting in enough to see us over the holiday, and when I got home — you see, I had my big umbrella with me — you know the one, I've had it all these years — and when I —'

'And when you got home, you found —' prompted Deborah, 'you found that — Granny, what's the matter? Are you feeling all right?'

Granny was staring out of the window, her lips slightly parted, one hand clutching her throat.

'*Granny!*'

Granny shook her head, ran her hand over her forehead, raised her eyebrows. 'What's that you're saying, Debbie? Go on reading to me again, will you, love? From the Christian Science Handbook.'

The truth was that she had just seen her husband

walking along the pavement, outside the window where the lime trees grew. It was very queer. She often saw him now. When she went shopping, for instance, she would see him on the other side of the street, smiling across at her.

But she didn't mention it to anybody. Her daughters would only worry and say she must be over-taxing her brain, or something. They could not be expected to understand that she was moving towards a greater reality where the invisible became visible at last. She had read how William Blake sat by his brother's death-bed and saw his brother's soul rise up through the ceiling clapping its wings for joy as it went. People said this was madness. But it wasn't — far from it! Her daughters would think these were the fancies of a tired old woman. Tired? Old? Oh no! There were mornings of birds and buds when she felt so young and strong that she wanted to dance for joy and would have rushed out into the garden singing if only her silly legs hadn't so obstinately refused to hurry.

Christmas that year was better than it had been for a long time. The family seemed to have settled down into an even period of work and modest prosperity. Commissions flowed steadily in for the artists, John added another layer of Persian and Afghanistan rugs in his rooms, time had partially healed the gap left by Diana. The sisters-in-law had accepted the grit in their diet, had accepted Mollie, from whom, apparently, John was not destined to escape.

That year everyone tried to work up a festive atmosphere. Angus decorated the tree, Joyce rehearsed Bruce and Jocelyn with carols. Salisbury had this triumphant present he'd been working on all through the autumn and Granny had Charles, her first great-grandchild. Johnnie brought a hamper of food in the Daimler. Even Dorothy consented to come, putting on her brittle armour of wit, praying she would get through the party without losing her temper or being sarcastic. She knew her worst side often showed itself among Bernard's people. Perhaps this was because they knew so much about her and pretence was impossible; even her jokes seemed to fall flat in the family and her usual sense of fun deserted her. She felt very vulnerable, but because Bernard begged her to come — 'For Ralph's sake, my dear —' she forced a smile across her face and vowed to keep off politics, at least.

Even so, it was a ghost of those bumper Christmases of the past, a subdued, muffled affair.

The great-aunts were there first, as usual — Dooley, Tabby, Kennedy, Sophia — but they were only black-and-white and one-dimensional now, death having transformed them into photographs on the mantelpiece. Granny's famous lap looked hollow, as though she were imitating some figure of Henry Moore's, and her face anxious as though expecting bad news. But when Betty put baby Charles into her arms a lovely change took place in her: a delicate blush warmed her face and throat and her features softened as an expression of great sweetness informed them. She made gentle little clucking noises and the baby stopped whimpering and fidgeting, as babies always did with her, and gazed up at her, grabbing for her nose and gurgling. The sisters gathered round her, cherishing the old life and the new. Reggie, Salisbury and Bernard stood talking about art. Mollie stayed as close to her young man as possible. Dorothy sat by herself, rather stiff, her hands folded in her lap, watching Ralph, who was wandering from group to group, grinning all over his bony face in a way that she found most heartening

187

and attractive. Betty and Sarah chatted about clothes and people, while the newcomer, Betty's Brazilian husband James, leaned against the wall and smiled at everyone. Tall, slender, pink and white and blond, James looked a typical Anglo-Saxon; people found it hard to believe that his forefathers came from such a savage part of the globe with its unexplored jungles, its unknown tribes, its fabulous wealth and degraded poverty. He seemed perfectly at home in this gathering. Deborah withdrew herself almost completely from the party. Standing alone by the window, she looked out into the lamp-lit streets, hoping that her friend, Billy, who was going to take her to a dance that evening, might come early. She wore a long dress and round her waist a beautiful belt she had made herself, a pretty fancy sewn all over with coloured glass that flashed and gleamed like jewels. Radiant with anticipation she looked almost glamorous.

Certain aspects remained completely unchanged, however. The fire still roared up the chimney like a tiger; the smell was the same — cinnamon, apples, resin from the fir-tree, the penetrating, subtle fragrance from the leaves of the *Pelargonium Capitatum* that Deborah was absently rubbing between her fingers. Nor had the expression on people's faces altered very much, even though hair had turned grey, or vanished altogether, though pain had set rows of little puckers round the lips and age clapped thick glasses on to fading eyes.

Perhaps Bernard had changed least of anyone. In fact, it might almost be said that he looked younger than in previous years. All the autumn he had been working high up on the scaffolding of a new building overlooking the Thames, putting the finishing touches to a Portland stone man staring out across the river, over the masts and the cranes downstream towards the open sea where Bernard's restless mind could always find peace. It has been said that between sea-faring people and artists a great kinship exists, as though they share a willingness to follow a vocation in which personal profit takes second place, as though they tacitly accept a discipline harsher than in most other ways of living. The case of Bernard could well add weight to that theory. The vision of open water he had from the scaffolding lent a liveliness to his expression, the fresh air and strenuous exercise kept him slim and supple and his complexion was less sallow than it used to be.

'How do you do it, old chap?' asked Salisbury. 'What's your secret of eternal youth?'

'Work. Nothing but work, work, work.'

'You look terrific. Not a grey hair to be seen!' Salisbury examined him closely, turning him round like a model. He himself was not looking very well. He coughed a great deal and often had a scooped-out appearance, as though some invisible enemy were worrying away at him and sapping his vitality. Clara beseeched him, in vain, to give up his heavy smoking; she was not happy about his health.

Granny started crooning to Charles the only song she could remember at that moment:

'Ten o'clock, the rain begins to fall
And Nellie still from home —'

'What really interests *me* —' In the big arm-chair by the fire John shook off his lethargy. '— are these experiments for television. It's *the* thing for the future. If I were a young man —'

'Do you know?' interrupted Ralph, his green eyes shining with excitement, 'that a day on Jupiter only last ten hours?'

'Does it, darlin'?' gasped Mollie.

'— yes, if I were young and had my force,' continued John, 'television's the thing I'd go in for. It'll open up the world. Enlarge understanding. It's a great power for progress.'

'All those pictures in the air?' Salisbury shook his head. 'No, it's impossible. Can't be done. It's beyond human endeavour. Just a myth.'

'My dear Salisbury, it's already on the way. Ten years and you'll be watching lovely sexy chorus girls without having to stir from your fireside.'

'Don't get excited, your Majesty,' soothed Mollie as John started to bellow out the truth of his vision.

'No,' persisted Salisbury. 'I've given it a lot of thought and I wouldn't know how to make a television set. It's not possible.'

Anything that Salisbury was unable to make himself was a snare and a delusion. He dismissed television as a fairy-story.

'Set of idiots!' shouted John, suddenly irritated. 'Narrow-minded ignoramuses! Maud, take that soppy expression off your face! Dorothy, what price Spain now? Your friends seem to have lost their little skirmish, don't they?'

Dorothy made a supreme effort. She lowered her eyes and looked fixedly down at her tightly folded hands. A verse of Housman's flashed into her mind:

> Some can gaze and not be sick
> But I could never learn the trick;
> There's this to say for life and breath
> They give a man a taste for death.

'And it'll be our turn next, Johnnie,' said Bernard politely, surprisingly coming to Dorothy's rescue. 'It'll be our turn to lose the little skirmish unless somebody stops Herr Hitler trampling across Europe.'

'Do you know —' Ralph leant forward, arms on knees, 'that nearly all the world conquerors have come out of Mongolia, Genghis Khan, Attila —'

'Tenderly her loving name we call,' hummed Granny, 'O whither does she roam —'

'I do wish I could find out what happened to Nellie,' Betty whispered to her husband.

'Your grandmother's so thoughtful,' answered James, *sotto voce*. 'When I went along to the lavatory just now the pieces of paper were labelled *back* and *front!* Charming of her!'

'Dear Granny and her dress-making patterns! She never throws anything away, you know. Bits of string too small to be of any use. Odd pieces of soap — odds and ends of elastic —'

'I'm skirmishing with the ants at present,' Dorothy at last brought out quietly. 'Specially in the summer. They're invading the house. It's a dreadful nuisance.'

'In olden times people used to distil red ants to make formic acid.' said Ralph seriously.

Dorothy looked across at his face, a mobile face always changing its expression, lit up by a multitude of thoughts and feelings, and she felt better.

John shrugged his shoulders. 'Let's have tea,' he ordered. 'Mollie, tea!'

After tea, when the lights on the tree shone again and Joyce banked up the fire to gargantuan proportions and Mollie passed round a flaring dish of snapdragon the party did seem to recapture some of the spontaneous gaiety of former times. Joyce played a mazurka on the Bechstein, Granny distributed her lavender bags and repeated how happy she was living here and how kind John had been to give her such a nice home. John smiled enigmatically, patted her cheek and said, 'You deserve it, *liebling*!' The aunts and cousins pushed little packages at each other and Salisbury laid his vast parcel on the floor in front of the baby, who was peacefully asleep on a cushion. Everyone else was agog to see what it was, however, and crowded round as he unwrapped his *pièce de résistance*, feeling sure his surprise would not be a disappointment.

This was Salisbury at his very best — a delicious piece of imagination, worked out with loving care down to the last precise detail, fresh as a rainbow.

It was a circus, a perfect model made from wood, wire, feathers, string, scraps of material, abandoned toy wheels and all sorts of other carefully hoarded flotsam from the cupboards in Salisbury's studio.

In the very centre of the arena, under a pink-and-white-striped awning, sat a lion and lioness in a cage. Round the edge were the performers — a pair of tumblers, a man strapped to the spokes of a wheel, an athlete balancing on a ball, a ballet dancer on a horse, a man pedalling a one-wheeled cycle. At the four corners of the little platform stood a clown holding up a hoop, a seal with a ball on his nose, John Bull with a flag, a red-nosed comic with a drum.

Salisbury touched a switch and tiny coloured lights shone all round the edge of the awning. He produced a handle, slotted it into the side of the platform and started to wind.

And the circus came to life.

The red-nosed clown beat his drum, blue-jacketed John Bull waved the flag, the ball wobbled on the seal's nose and, wonder of wonders, the dainty *equestrienne* leapt neatly through the hoop and as her white horse pranced along his mane, made of little feathers, blew back in the breeze he created. The tumblers tumbled, the man spun round within his wheel — all the carved and painted people performed their appointed tricks, going round and round the arena, smoothly circling the cage containing the good-tempered lion and lioness.

Baby Charles slept on, undisturbed by the excitement of the others as they jostled for turns at winding up his toy.

'Should we play some games?' suggested Joyce after a while. 'Or how about some carols?'

No one responded. The young children were still too engrossed in the circus. It was almost as good as the real thing. They lay flat on the floor on their tummies and pretended to be part of that miniature world, imagined themselves into the role of minute spectators, chuckled to themselves contentedly as they gave tiny shouts of applause and made clapping sounds with their finger nails. Betty and Sarah and James sat on the sofa gossiping. Deborah had resumed her stand by the window again and was starting to look worried. Suppose Billy didn't come. Suppose he'd had an accident on the way. Or, worse still, suppose he wasn't really serious. Mollie and Dorothy went into the kitchen to start the washing-up.

'It's good to see you again, me sweetheart. You've been keeping yourself so private all these years. How are you, darlin'? And how's Vicky getting on abroad?'

'In her last letter she said that Madame had been busy making a crib for Christmas and that Monsieur was going to cook the Christmas dinner. But to tell you the truth, Mollie, I'm worried about her.'

'Oh no, what's the matter?'

'This summer we had to go out specially to stop her getting engaged to some young man she'd picked up. She's only seventeen. And now it seems there's another one. I'd always thought she was so sensible.'

'She'll be all right. She's probably only doing it as a protest. Or to prove she can.'

'It seems so silly of her. It's such a worry. I was never like that. Oh, Mollie, all this man and woman business is just a necessary evil. What really matters is man and man, woman and woman.'

'You may be right, darlin'. My young man certainly knocked the stuffing out of me.'

'I blame Granny for most of that,' said Dorothy quickly.

'I don't know we can blame anyone. I mean, we're all in this life together.'

Dorothy caught her breath. She, of all people, ought not to talk about blaming people. She remembered a sequence of events, many years ago, just before she married Bernard, about which she had never spoken to anyone, of which only her closest friends knew. She sometimes thought Diana had been punished for her own sin of fear that summer afternoon of long ago, when the dusty road stretched ahead of her and a sensation of loss and panic made her lose her head.

'No, no, no,' she pushed back her unwelcome thoughts. 'You're right, Mollie. Quite right. You know, I don't always think before I speak. I've got a dreadfully sharp tongue, you know.' 'I mean, I don't expect Granny wanted to be left with those five babies, all alone without her young man,' continued Mollie. 'Life must have been bitterly hard for her sometimes. I've got nothing to thank her for. She made my life hell. But it's no good hugging griefs for ever. Now then, I'm sure young Vickers'll be all right.'

'It's very worrying. I don't know what she can be thinking of.'

Vicky was thinking of a great deal. It would be a

long time, however, before she could understand the reasons that made her behave in such a disconcerting way.

'And don't you think, Dorothy, these young ones have lived so long with the talk of wars — wars past and the threat of wars to come. Perhaps she's just packing all she can into the present?'

Mollie's morals were much more flexible than Dorothy's and her attitude to sex altogether different. It did sometimes occur to her to wonder if perhaps Dorothy set people impossibly high standards of behaviour, that in trying to reach up to these her children kept on slipping and felt absurdly guilty at their failure.

'Mollie — I couldn't bear to lose — to lose another child.'

'You won't, darlin', you won't. Listen — if that isn't my young man singing a negro spiritual! Hasn't he got a gorgeous voice! I'm going back into the drawing-room.'

They crept back and sat down while John went on singing softly and with great feeling, accompanying himself on the piano.

> 'Swing low, sweet chariot,
> Coming for to carry me home —
> Sw — hing low, sweet chari — o — ot —'

When that spiritual was finished he went on to another and then another. It was not exactly Christmas, but it was uncommonly moving.

Deborah, still standing by the window, cried out in a voice that trembled with excitement, 'Here's Billy! Look, he's come. He's coming up the front steps. I'll go and let him in.'

She hurried from the room, returning hand in hand

with a dark, quick, clever-looking boy: she led him first of all to Granny to pay his respects and he presented her with a package beautifully tied with bright ribbon.

'What's this?' she asked.

'Ah ha!' Billy smiled wickedly.

'Unwrap it, Granny,' said Deborah. 'He's like Daddy. It's a surprise!'

'Here, let me,' said Billy as Granny fumbled and exclaimed. 'Do you mind if I stand on a chair?'

He reached up towards the light fixture in the middle of the room and swiftly and deftly fastened something to it. A charming little Christmas decoration swung below the lamp, paper figures, brightly coloured, that swayed and bobbed in the currents of air.

'Oh, there —' cried Granny. 'Did you make it yourself.'

'Yes, he did,' Deborah answered for him while Billy, suddenly shy, stood grinning and twisting his hands.

'Oh, aren't you original?' said Granny, immediately accepting him as one of the family.

The newcomer, however, broke up the party. Betty said it was time she and James took the baby home, Maud told Reggie to go and phone for a taxi because Sawah was going out to a gwand dinner tonight and didn't want to huwwy over her dwessing. Ralph gave a happy sigh and said loudly. 'Thank goodness, that's all finished now!' And Dorothy shot him a grateful, sympathetic glance.

'Our car'll be here any minute now,' said Mollie, 'I told the chauffeur sharp at six. Can we give anybody a lift.'

'We're not going anybody else's way,' said John firmly.

'Joyce, you don't have to go yet?' As always, Granny hated to see them all putting on their coats, tried to stave off those horrid minutes when they would all turn their back and walk away and she would have to shut the front door behind them and once more be alone.

'Well, Mother, I'll just stay and clear up a little. But we can't stay much longer. Jocelyn's got a bit of a cold.'

'We'll have another party soon, Granny,' promised Salisbury. 'Perhaps it'll be an engagement party!' And he gave her a knowing wink.

'Hush, Salisbury,' admonished Clara. 'They'll hear you. You don't want to make Deborah feel embarrassed. Anyway, they're both so young.'

'Another party, another party!' joked Salisbury, covering up his mistake. 'Have we all had our silver weddings, by the way?

Talking and laughing, they all left the house, turning as they reached the front gate to look back into the warm room, to wave to Granny peering rather wanly through the windowpane.

This was the last party they ever had at Oxford Road. As a matter of fact there was only to be one more family conclave. No, two — but at the second gathering the most important person would not be there.

CHAPTER TEN

YES, the following year the war came, to force their lives into new directions and scatter them all about the place. The old warmth and family unity was almost at an end.

'And you, Ralph?' asked Bernard, from the depths of the transformed Pembroke Walk dining-room, sandbagged and timber-propped against bombs. 'Do you want to be evacuated? We could afford to send you to safety. To America. Quite a lot of school children are going.'

Ralph's reply was adamant. 'I may still be at school. But I'm not a child. And until Germany has been bled white — and I hope to take part in that procedure — I refuse to quit our dear Fatherland.'

He was, actually, longing to visit America, but had made up his mind he'd get there somehow under his own steam. Although barely fifteen, he was wishing he could volunteer for active service. He would stand in front of the mirror examining his face and wondering how he could wangle his age. But he had to admit that it could not be done. He had the youthful, almost dewy, looks that are so often the lot of the very fair; his hair was fine and silky as a girl's, his forehead unlined and he had not even the smallest scar to lend him a fierce and interesting air. Although he hopefully scraped away at his chin two or three times a week no corn-coloured stubble broke through the skin. Danger and excitement called to him in loud voices; he felt frustrated that he could not yet respond to them. In some ways he was to have the most adventurous and unorthodox life of anyone in the family. Like his mother he wanted to sacrifice himself for some great cause, although, unlike her, he would never be able to espouse himself to the common lot of mankind, nor devote himself to working for the greater good of humanity. He followed an unusual and lonely path. From an early age he charmed and interested many people and, again like Dorothy, cared not one whit for the opinion of others. A friend of the family even considered making Ralph his heir, as he had no children of his own. Hoping to get better acquainted with the lively, green-eyed boy, he invited him to lunch one day at the Athenaeum. Once was enough.

'Do you know —' his voice expressed mortal pain, 'that Ralph Seabridge eats his peas on his knife.'

He won many prizes at school, did his best at games. But no art for him — no fear! He was fed up with art. He purposefully turned his young face away from sculpture, painting, music, poetry and all that rot and cultivated the rude techniques of philistinism. For him it was to be the seams of mineral wealth in the earth, for him the beckoning light of stars beyond this solar system.

'Perhaps Australia?' tried Bernard, secretly proud of his patriotic son.

'No bloody fear! Anyway, the school's moving away, worst luck. To Hereford, or somewhere equally sunk.

But I do think you ought to look after Mummy. You ought to see she goes somewhere safe in the country.' He gave Bernard a long, narrow stare. 'I'm sure you've got the money.'

He suspected Bernard was unnecessarily mean about money and he believed that he treated Dorothy shabbily. Dorothy had this compulsion to talk — to express her private troubles — and when Vicky wasn't around to listen she confided in Ralph. He was growing up to hate and distrust his father and to feel an exaggerated sense of responsibility for his mother. A tangle of loyalties was weaving around him, twisting and inhibiting.

Dorothy went off to the Chilterns to see if she could find a refuge for them if times got really bad.

Bernard volunteered to be an air-raid warden and he started on his long, slow read right the way through the non-fiction section of the Kensington Public Library.

Vicky started to learn all the poems of Wilfred Owen by heart, joined the anarchists, said, 'I think I'll volunteer for one of the nursing services,' got herself a job on a magazine giving advice to mothers, and generally went on acting in a mixed-up way.

Deborah, engaged to Billy, came rushing home one day beaming with happiness. 'Isn't it marvellous, Mummy! Billy's C.3!'

Betty's A.1 husband was called up into the Army and disappeared for the duration: Betty took baby Charles away to the country.

The world roared about Sarah. She felt disturbingly adrift and longed to anchor herself. She was twenty-seven and it was high time she was married. For all her wit and glamour, however, this did not come about easily; the man to whom she was most drawn already had a wife. She used to stand at her bedroom window drumming on the glass, feeling frustrated and a little fearful because life seemed to be slipping away faster and faster.

Reggie and Maud went north with the Royal College of Art.

Joyce and her boys went to Cornwall.

Mollie and Johnnie stayed put.

And Granny?

Poor Granny — the most horrible experience of her life pounced down to make her utterly wretched. She was uprooted from her Bechstein, from the fragrant geranium in its two-handled brass container, from the scent of limes that came in at the open window after a shower, and she was hurled into the outer darkness of solitude in Wimbledon.

'Oxford Road's not safe,' said Johnnie. 'I don't like to think of you being alone here. I've found two rooms for you. In Wimbledon.'

'But Johnnie, Wimbledon's no safer than Putney.'

'All the same, you've got to go. I insist.'

'Johnnie, love, you can't turn me out,' she protested weakly. 'It's my *home*.'

'It may be your home, Mother, but it's my *house*.'

'Yours? I don't understand. I've been paying the mortgage every month. For years.'

'And who's been giving you the money to pay the mortgage?'

'You've always been so generous, Johnnie. I paid it out of the allowance you give me. And dear little Bernard he always gives me an allowance too. Not as much as you. But then he has got a family to bring up, hasn't he.'

'I don't care how much dear little Bernard gives you, Mother. I know I've kept you going ever since I was about sixteen. I had to work like a fiend, you know. I didn't mind, but you can't expect me to do everything for nothing. Oxford Road's mine. You've been buying the house for *me* with *my* money.'

'What do you mean, Johnnie? You've got a house.'

He smiled at her rather forlornly and put his arms round her. 'Don't let's quarrel, *liebling*. You know I've always loved you more than anyone else. Sweetheart, I'll feel happier if you're in Wimbledon. I've found two nice little rooms all ready for you. And you do want to make me happy, don't you, *mein Schatz*?'

A more autocratic old lady than Granny would have stamped her foot and said, 'Over my dead body! I'll leave this house in my coffin, thank you!' Being the sort of person she was, however, she merely turned pale with terror and went to pack her bits and pieces.

She was intensely miserable in her two-roomed flat where the walls lacked the familiar paintings, where the doors were in the wrong places and let in draughts and where the lavatory was much too far away. She spent most of her time there hunched up in an uncomfortable chair behind a screen, cowering like a frightened cat.

Eventually Bernard came to her rescue with the practical suggestion that she move into Buckinghamshire, up on to those chalky, majestic Chilterns where Dorothy had managed to find a *pied à terre*. The village policeman said he had a spare room, a nice homely room where Granny could make herself very comfy: and he and Dorothy, said Bernard, cycling between London and their three attic rooms at the top of an old farmhouse, would be near at hand if she wanted anything.

With the cohesion that war always brings, the personal tensions of Bernard and Dorothy began to ease and the burden of guilt they had silently shared between them for the last six or seven years slid away little by little. A breath of geniality, almost of tenderness, began to seep through here and there.

They could share the rediscovered emotion of patriotism; sometimes the fiercest critics of a country transform themselves into the truest lovers. They could share a loving anxiety for friends in battle areas. Each dawn, after a bombardment, they could share the joy of renewed life; and they found the same sort of pleasure in war-time conditions.

They enjoyed the dark nights, those unexpectedly lovely velvety skies when London was lit only by the stars or by the frosty glamour of the moon. They liked the quiet, empty streets and both took to their bicycles again with great vigour.

Rationing pleased Dorothy. The equal sharing out satisfied her socialist ideals, the necessity for managing on very little gratified her puritanical nature. She could skimp, manage, contrive and cheese-pare and for once, the Lord be praised, it was the right thing to do. No longer compelled to arouse the starvelings from their slumbers to grapple with the menace of Nazism, she directed her energies into more conventional channels, such as helping in canteens and making bread. Her brown bread was delicious. Dough, covered with old pieces of blanket, was always rising in her kitchen and the air was sweet with freshly-baked bread — that good, healthy smell that, like the smell of wood smoke, brings to everyone such a host of delightful associations.

In sundry little ways they drew closer again. Ralph's distinction at school and his firm character gave them mutual content and pride. Bernard, temporarily relieved from the ceaseless competition of wresting a living from inclement stone, grew kinder as the sharp edge of personal ambition stopped tormenting him.

Perhaps the happiest times of all came to them at summer week-ends — Bernard refused to leave London during the week, come incendiaries or high explosives — when they rose before dawn and took to their bikes, going out to Buckinghamshire along deserted main roads. Those were wonderful rides in the tremulous morning air, with the larks showering down songs on them and the sharp fragrance of growing corn catching at their nostrils as they pedalled past the fields on their ten-mile-an-hour rush towards the Chilterns.

Bledlow Ridge was a heavenly place. Dorothy had always wanted somewhere in the country and she made the most of her week-ends there. The atmosphere was fine and dry; she could see for miles into the blue distance. She found meadows where cowslips grew, tangled banks where wild violets hid, hillsides that shone with glow-worms on summer nights. It was an austere, noble countryside, much to her taste, with crests of beech woods along some of the hills and silent, secret valleys where black-eyed gipsies camped. In summer the smell of grass and clover filled every cranny of the whitewashed attics: in winter the free wind hurled itself across the hills and with her face turned towards the Pole star, that magnet of her soul, she could drink in air as pure and icy as mountain water. The essential charm and graciousness of her nature came to the surface again; her sense of humour bubbled up spontaneously. She made many new friends. She adored Bledlow.

Granny was not so enthusiastic. Salisbury saved up petrol and she complainingly sat by his side while he drove her gently along to the village policeman's cottage.

'There won't be any bombs here, Granny,' he en-couraged her. 'It's safer than Wimbledon or Putney. You'll be able to sleep in peace.'

'My neuralgia won't let me sleep,' she grumbled. 'It's much worse than the bombs.'

'You'll be warm and cosy. And you won't have to bother about any shopping or cooking.'

'I expect they'll have an outside lavatory. What'll I do in the night? How'll I manage when it rains?'

'You've got all your luggage, haven't you? You'll be all right.'

'Yes, I think I've remembered everything.'

She turned round to look. On the back seat Salisbury had put her *Pelargonium capitatum* in its brass container, her large, black umbrella, three cases, her chamber-pot, a blue rug and two wide-brimmed hats.

'You'll love it, Granny, really you will. Bernard'll be here at week-ends and one of us'll come down to see you every week. And we'll all be happy because we'll know you're safe.'

But all those miles away from her usual haunts, with no commanding telephone bell to bring her news, she was almost more unhappy than she had been in Wimble-don. She had not got it in her to rage or to fuss; she merely shrivelled up.

So, when the war settled down to that long, dreary wait for the second front and life began to dribble back to an approximation of normal John said that Granny might as well return to Oxford Road. She same back gleefully, with her umbrella, her chamber-pot, her pelargonium and all her other chattels, and she resumed her cultivation of herbs and lavender, knitted body belts for her great-grandson and prayed for the safety of her scattered darlings who didn't write nearly as often as she wished they would. She adored getting letters. She read them with the aid of a strong magnifying glass and always answered them the same day.

'Are you going to Sarah's wedding?' Vicky asked her mother in the autumn of 1941.

'There's one thing that really makes life worth living,' replied Dorothy, sitting on the edge of the kitchen sink peeling potatoes, 'and that's doing a job supremely well. Carving a statue, writing a poem, peeling potatoes, baking —'

'Yes, I know. But are you going?'

'No, I'm not. I refused to go to Betty's and so it wouldn't be fair if I went to Sarah's.'

'Do you mind if I go?'

'Of course I don't, darling. Your father'll be going. You can wear your pretty lime-green dress, can't you. Have you seen the papers today? Terrible Russian losses in the Ukraine. I can't bear to think of it. Did you read that in the Donetz basin rain's been falling for twenty days? The battlefield's a swamp and the dead remain unburied. And we do nothing. Nothing. It's dreadful. We send safety-pins to the Russians, we send hot-water bottles to the Russians, we even honour them by calling them our Allies. But we *do* nothing.'

'Perhaps we're not ready to do anything yet.'

'People everywhere are getting discontented with the way things are going. It just needs a spark to set the world alight.'

'But where's the spark to come from?'

'From some great leader of the people.'

'I wonder if there's anyone with enough sparks left in them.'

England of 1941 was a world of weariness and frustration. Bogged down by inaction, people waited and waited, while Wellingtons and Spitfires crashed in flames, the great Russian cities were razed to the ground, famous ships were sunk. The battleship on which Bernard had so jauntily toured the Mediterranean, H.M.S. *Repulse*, had gone down and the seas had taken for ever his gay friend, the handsome, blue-eyed, black-haired Commander. Unspeakable rumours seeped out from occupied countries. Now and again a hard flash of personal news would blaze out from the perimeter of darkness.

'My brother — he left Germany when I did and practised medicine in Paris. I haven't heard a word from him since the fall of France —'

'This convoy route to Russia is pure hell. We feel cold all the time. The kites we fly are done up with string. You can't imagine what we feel like as we sit there in our cockpits waiting to take off. We know if we're shot down into that icy sea we haven't a chance —'

'Our son — he's been reported missing in Africa. My wife's going mental about it. She sits up in bed in the middle of the night and she cries "Oh, what'll he do about cleaning his teeth, he won't have a toothbrush with him and he was always so fussy about cleaning his teeth —" '

'The girls at school keep asking me about my parents — why don't they write to me, they ask? And I say Vienna's such a long way away, another country. I'll give them another six months to write. And then, if they don't, I'll know, I'll know — oh no, I can't bear to think about it —'

However, in the midst of foreboding and exhaustion Sarah had at last come to sensible terms with the realities of her private destiny. She had given up trying to reach that tantalizing image of perfect love and fulfilment that existed, apparently, just beyond her grasp and had decided to settle for the second best.

This second best was really very suitable — rich, well-connected, devoted. She could not lose herself in him, he did not transport her beyond the common-places of love; here and there they clashed and she sometimes felt in him a curious coldness, a turning away from all social contacts that frightened her. She was, however, a balanced, sweet-tempered person and she believed they could make a go of it.

So she sewed herself a wedding dress and an ex-quisite trousseau, made up her face with the skill of an artist and, looking remarkably lovely, beamed at her bridegroom and made all the usual promises. For some reason her eyes, normally a shining brown, were yellow as a leopard's that day.

Later the family, loyally gathered together from all over the country, drank champagne and ate tiny sand-wiches at the reception in a Knightsbridge hotel. Reggie made a stately, mannered father-of-the-bride and Maud, looking a picture in her silks and furs and overjoyed that at last her daughter was settling down, smiled to left and to right and wherever she looked — at the window panes, at the shining coffee spoons, into the eyes of the guests — her enchanting reflection smiled back. All the sisters were wearing good fur coats; it was a far cry from the specially-reduced-for-you bar-gains of their childhood. Granny had fur trimmings and a foxy creature round her shoulders; she sat near the tables and ate as much as she could. Johnnie opened the sandwiches and looked at their contents before eating; if he didn't like what he saw he put it back on the plate. He had, recently, suffered a minor stroke and had to be very careful about everything, including what he ate. His favourite recreation was wandering through the food departments of Harrods and Selfridges, gloat-ing over the delicacies he was warned to avoid, rich delicacies that the shops managed to procure now and then in spite of the war.

'And how's Ralph?' Reggie asked Bernard. 'Called up yet?'

'To our relief and his regret he's not eligible for another eighteen months. And the war may be over by then.'

'You're hopeful, dear boy!'

'Far from it. I'm becoming more and more of a pessimist. We're on the decline and there's nothing we can do about it.'

'Come now, it's not as bad as that. Will Ralph fulfil your personal ambitions and choose the Navy?'

'He says it's to be the Fleet Air Arm. He wants to fly. He tells me this is the most dangerous service. And he wants to give as much as he can for his country.'

'He wants that, does he? Well, Bernard old chap, while there're such fine boys with noble feelings like that you can tell your beastly old German, Herr Spengler, that he can go to blazes. We're far from being on the decline.'

'He means the whole of Western civilization — the great sweep of it, historical as well as geographical. But Reggie, you may be right. Something may happen —' Bernard's alert mind was always open to new currents, new possibilities: he never closed up around his ideas, nor allowed them to harden into dogmas. 'Yes, we may arise — some great and good energy may be astir. Some force may be at work at this very moment, in hidden places where we can't see — I've been reading Browning lately, Reggie. Interesting poet! So vigorous!'

'So you and Billy really are going to get married, Deborah love?' queried Granny.

'Yes, Granny. Next year if possible.' Although

Deborah was nearly twenty-three and a qualified architect she did not look old enough to get married. She
had inherited in full measure the family characteristic
of a youthful appearance.

'Won't Billy have to go and fight? Isn't it better to
wait till the end of the war?'

'Billy's exempt, Granny. I did tell you. Don't you
remember? Isn't it marvellous?'

'So you did. That'll be a blessing for you.'

'By the way, Reggie,' Bernard raised his second glass
of champagne to his lips. 'Don't mention to Dorothy
about Ralph going into the Fleet Air Arm. He doesn't
want her to know yet. She's such a worrier.'

'You're not going to marry that foreign young man I
met down at Bledlow, are you love?' Granny peered at
Vicky. 'That Jewish refugee?'

Vicky winced and chewed a sandwich. She didn't
want to talk about this latest cause of trouble at home.

'He chatted to me so nicely, there in the policeman's
cottage. I could tell he was very clever. And a very
handsome man. Yes, very handsome. I could see that,
even without my glasses on.'

There had been a blistering row when it was discovered that, caught by the sirens and the throbbing of
the German bombers, they had spent a whole night
alone together. Bernard, not really anti-Semitic, too
gentle to be militantly anti-anything, except bad art and
shoddy standards had raged like a Victorian papa and
threatened to cut her off without a penny if she married
this seductive foreigner, this stranger fleeing from the
maelstrom who had to live on his wits for the time being,
who was as much an outcast as Vicky so often felt herself
to be and with whom she felt a real affinity. The memory
of that other Jewish incursion into the affections of a
child probably touched Bernard on nerves still raw,

inflaming and distorting his emotions. Dorothy had stood by him, wringing her hands, her face as ashen and drawn as it had been on that terrible morning of Diana's death, a face that was indelibly printed on Vicky's memory and from which she was never altogether to escape.

'I mean, love, marrying a foreigner — these days — It's very risky. You don't really know anything about him.'

Granny was a silly old bore, a platitudinous gas-bag. All she could give advice on was how to wash hair so it kept its colour, or how to turn up a hem in double quick time. When it came to real difficulties, to questions of love and duty, sacrifice and expiation, of straightening out the twists of right and wrong, she wasn't an earthly bit of good. You might as well try talking to her umbrella. She just didn't catch on.

'No, Granny, I'm not going to marry him.'

No, she simply hadn't been able to bring herself to do that to her parents. Whether she was being weak or strong, she didn't know, but to go against their deeply-felt prejudices and terrors was an impossibility for her. It might kill her mother. Sometimes she felt she was going to go on paying for her sister's death with every chance of happiness that came her way. Or was that just a conveniently melodramatic peg on which to hang her failures? She was mercilessly pinned on the horns of a dilemma. The very causes that drove her to seek her friends on the fringes of society made it almost impossible for her ever to break away from her family. Muffled up, speechless under the influence of family troubles that had probably started long before she was born, she batted about wildly in the dark.

'I'm glad, Vicky love, I'm glad. You're making the right decision.'

'I don't know that I am —' She turned away and found herself face to face with Mollie. The relief of seeing that hot, jolly face was so great that she almost hugged her. Then, instantly, she remembered the fur muff at home in her cupboard and hoped she wouldn't be asked why she wasn't wearing it. The rest of the family was, after all, decked out in animal skins.

But Mollie said: 'I hear you're really going off to be a nurse at last.'

'Yes, next week, actually. Civil nursing reserve.'

'What are your doing it for, Vickers? Your country?'

'Well — er — not exactly. More for humanity really.'

'Oh well, it's healthy to be idealistic while you're young. You know I was a Red Cross nurse once, don't you?'

'You?'

'Yes, darlin'. When my young man and I were flee-ing from the Bolshies the train we were on came to a dead stop in Siberia. In the middle of a battlefield.'

'Ooooh!'

'Yes, all that snow and ice. And bangs going on all round. And groans. I've forgotten who the battle was between. But there was a battle. We turned the train into a hospital. And I put on a uniform. And a red cross. And I bandaged wounds.'

'Goodness!'

'You should have heard the wolves at night, Vickers. And the bears!'

Dear, rosy-nosed Mollie. Vicky was thankful for her and she followed her around, basking in the warmth of her personality with its aroma of alcohol. She felt suffi-ciently encouraged to approach Bernard and suggest they might go on to see *Alexander Nevski* at the Academy Cinema when the reception petered out.

'Oh no, my dear, I really haven't got the time.' Bernard turned to Johnnie with a wry smile. 'You know, I'm in a fever to get home and go on working.'

John nodded and the two brothers exchanged a deep look — John corpulent and flabby, sentimental, cunning, successful; Bernard slim and light-footed, reserved, honourable, obstinate. So different in appearance and in character, the brothers, nevertheless, shared this ferment of energy, this compulsion to go on and on. They had this common memory of early risings on bitter winter mornings, of their mother rushing round them in a whirlwind of daemonic energy saying, 'You must work, boys, work. We rely on you to make us rich, boys. Work!'

'What are you working on now, Bernard?'

'It's something I'm hoping will happen, John. It's a man emerging from the ruins of war, a superman who'll be better than we are. Come back to the studio with me and I'll show you. A man living and improving — in spite of everything. I'm calling it "Strands of Man". From the Gerard Manley Hopkins poem — Dorothy's very keen on him. You know — "Not untwist, slack they may be, these last strands of man —" and so on. I *must* believe this.'

'And you call yourself a pessimist!' Johnnie's voice was almost gentle and there were tears in his eyes as he looked at his vibrant young brother of fifty.

'I'll take you to the film, darlin'.' Mollie stepped into the breach, slipping her arm through Vicky's. 'Come on. We'll treat ourselves to a spree before you go off to work for your humanity. And my young man can drive your father back to his studio and have a look at this stone man of the future.'

'Perhaps I'm not an out-and-out pessimist,' agreed Bernard. 'Something marvellous may happen. A second

213

coming! Even —' and his voice dropped to a whisper '— even a second love.'

John would have liked to have said something like, 'And *really*, Bernard, how are things? Have you really come to terms? Are you happy?'

To which Bernard might have replied something like, 'Only a fool can be happy in times like these. Happiness — what is it? Life's very difficult and it's going to get more difficult. But yes, there are times, when a figure's coming to life out of a block of stone, or on a beautiful day in high summer — times when it all seems worth while.'

Instead John remonstrated, 'A second coming, Bernard? You don't believe all that stuff, do you? You're far too intelligent!'

'I'm not precisely sure exactly what I believe,' replied Bernard. 'I believe *dis aliter visum* — the gods see otherwise — and I have always bowed my head before the romance of destiny. But I do know that, for me, nothing more profound was ever said than, "My kingdom is not of this world." '

'They're off! They're going!' called Joyce. 'Doesn't Sarah look beautiful! Look, Mother, look — put on your other pair of glasses! Wave good-bye!'

'Oh —' cried Granny. 'Oh, oh!' Emotions charged through her frail body and blinding tears ran down her thin cheeks. Caught by a paroxysm of coughing, she vigorously waved her black umbrella in the direction of Sarah setting off on her new life.

'Careful, Granny,' said Angus. 'You nearly had my eye out. I'm going to see if I can find a taxi and then we'll take you home.'

'I do so hope Sarah'll be happy,' said Granny as they drove back to Oxford Road. 'I do so hate it when things go wrong for any of you. Do you think she will?

He's got a lot of money, hasn't he? That's always a help.'

'I'm sure she'll be very happy.' Joyce's voice, soothing as warm milk, reassured her. She wiped the rest of her tears from her eyes, blew her nose and started to recount all the nice things people at the reception had said to her — how young she looked, what lovely grandchildren she had, and how on earth did she manage to keep her hair still brown, not a grey streak in it, how?

'It really was a lovely wedding, wasn't it, Joyce? Ever so smart. Everyone was so kind to me.'

'You deserve it, dear. You're always so kind to people yourself.'

'Quite a grand affair, wasn't it. I hope there'll be some more weddings soon — soon — soon —' Granny's head nodded and she fell comfortably asleep, never to know that the grandest wedding of the family waited in the future, when, fifteen years later, Joyce's youngest son would be married in St. Paul's Cathedral with hundreds of guests. That was going to be a tremendous party.

In the studio Bernard led his brother up to the Portland stone man who cried 'Carrion!' to cold comfort despair, straining up out of the bondage of war towards the unknown. Chains fettered his ankles, his face was lined and suffering, his head bore a weight of ignorance and every stone fibre suggested effort and an agonized endurance.

'But he's not really successful.' Bernard turned quickly away from the carving. 'No, not a good piece of work.'

'You've still got your lovely girl, I see.' John walked across to the bronze figure of a young woman, her knees slightly bent, her arms up in the air almost as though she were stretching after sleep. 'She doesn't date.'

'My "Awakening"? Yes, I did her when I was young, just before I went into the Army in the last war. The classical influences were still breathing by my side, John! What a time that was to be alive, John — before that war that none of us could really foresee — not even Dorothy's political brother — you know, the one who was killed on the Somme.'

'Yes,' mused John. 'Yes. Remember that boat we built, Bernard? Launched it from the towing-path at Putney?'

'Creaky old tub!' laughed Bernard. 'But she carried us all right. But those mornings, John — waking up — there was a sense of freedom and the world opening out in front of one — such excitement in being alive. What is it today? *Le son du cor est trist au fond du bois* —'

'You're older now, Bernard.'

'Yes, Johnnie, I know that. But for our children — I don't see how it can possibly be what it was for us. The blissful illusions we nursed — the fun —'

John looked shrewdly at him. He remembered his brother as an undemonstrative, shy, serious young man with an unexpectedly waggish sense of humour; he had not thought of him as seething with joy and anticipation. How little one knew people!

'You could get a good price for this figure,' he said, reverting to the hard world of cash that he understood so well.

'I couldn't part with her. She's too much a part of my life.'

'What a romantic you are, Bernard!'

'I don't know about that. This girl's absolutely real — right down to the bones. I did her just as she was, a young model of seventeen or eighteen. I even did her feet exactly — rather ugly feet if you look carefully, rather too broad and splayed out. As a matter of fact I have a young friend, a young sailor, who's absolutely potty about her, completely enamoured. She's his Galatea all right. He's always coming round here and taking photographs. He asks me time and time again to sell her. Says he'll raise any sum I ask.'

'Then aren't you being rather selfish, keeping her all to yourself.'

'I shall leave her to the Tate Gallery in my will. They won't accept her, of course. Not their idea of sculpture. But the gods will find the right place for her to stand when I'm dead.'

'She's got Dorothy's face.' John put his hands on the slender bronze waist and looked up.

'The finest stage of sculpture was expressed in Greece in the fifth century B.C.,' Bernard shied away from this unaccustomed heart to heart with John and took flight to the clarity of the classical world. 'It's the exact union of the abstract value with the imitative power,' he said rather pedantically. 'You'll have to go to Reims Cathedral to see anything approaching this skill in the last thousand years. Or Wells. Or Lincoln.'

'Yes, you certainly have your visions.' John was loth to let the subject drop.

'When I am at work,' said Bernard quietly, 'I can believe I am better than I am. I can lose myself in the effort of creation and imagine I'm working towards some perfection of life.'

'Yes,' said John, 'we all have our visions. Mother must have had a vision of something when she carted us all off to Germany. And even I have had my dreams, you know. I'm not such a fool that I don't know what you all think of me. I know you think I'm a selfish, materialistic old bastard. But electricity and all that —

well, you know, it's done a lot towards making people's lives happier and easier. In the old days, when I saw mother working away, putting a brave face on it, slipping out at night to scrub the front doorstep and then pretending she'd never held a scrubbing-brush in her life — and on those Monday washdays when she slaved away at the tub — well, I used to vow I'd find some way of lightening her tasks. I used to look up at the sky and think, all that energy, all that energy doing nothing. I used to dream of harnessing shooting stars! All those women whose lives were one long drudgery, who weren't even able to keep milk from turning sour in thundery weather — I used to think of all the ways they could be helped — you know, electric power doing the work for them, and all that sort of thing. It's not my fault I got rich on the way. Is it?

Wanting money, Vicky made a last round-up of her possessions before she went off to nurse and sold nearly everything she had, including the enormous amethyst given her by the man she was not going to marry.

'What about that muff?' said Dorothy. 'In your cupboard. It'll get the moth in it.'

Dorothy's own personal war — against the ants — was becoming increasingly fierce. Ancient communities outside in the Lane and the courtyard, disturbed by bombs, were on the move, marching into her kitchen, devouring the food in the larder, refusing to be repelled by D.D.T. or boiling water. For survival it was imperative to put every scrap of food attractive to ants in the middle of large bowls of water. Ants could neither swim nor jump. This was all a great bother and Dorothy was acrimonious against the entire insect world.

Vicky took out the muff and shook it. It looked absurd and dejected, with a sort of crazy frenzy about it, like an amorous old woman. She doubted that anybody would want it. However, Mollie was wealthy and the fur had come from Russia so it might, conceivably, be valuable. She took a bus to the City.

The street where they traded in furs was a street for a murder and a chase, a street for despair and young lovers. It was perfectly straight and apparently endless, with green, damp steps leading down to the Thames, and doorways that enticed and warned. Most of the warehouses were anonymous, but a few had valiant names resounding with history and adventure, like the Hudson's Bay Company.

She tried them all. People looked at her as though she were an apparition and shook their heads. The man at the Universal Fur Company was kind enough to say, 'You won't sell that down 'ere, ducks. There's nobody wants nuffing like that. Try the West End.'

In the large West End stores buyers tapped their shiny shoes impatiently on the floor and spoke down their noses. With each supercilious rejection of the muff her determination, however, grew. At last someone asked her why she didn't try a certain address off Golden Square.

She knocked at a door that needed painting. An extraordinarily handsome young woman with an apricot-golden skin and a throat like a singer's answered, smiled, shook her head as though she were dumb, pushed open another door with her elbow and then rushed off somewhere downstairs.

Vicky stood on the threshold of a large, panelled room strewn with furs. A small, fat man sat at a maho-gany table eating poached eggs from a silver dish.

'Ah —' he held out his arms as though he had been expecting her.

'I want to sell this.' Vicky flung the muff on to the table where it lay like a silly, obstinate challenge.

The merchant pushed his mouth into a smile, his eyes remaining sorrowful and intense, like an over-worked child's. He stroked the muff with the back of his hand.

'I wouldn't give you ten shillings for it.' he said regretfully. 'Yes, perhaps it did come from Russia, but it must have been the Russia of Ivan the Terrible. Never, never have I seen such an ancient piece of fur. So an auntie gave it to you, did she? Well, well. And since when have relations ever given anything but awful presents?'

He picked it up, feeling it with sharp, small fingers. 'Poor little displaced fur, nobody's baby.' He wiped the egg off his mouth. 'I tell you what — she's not worth ten shillings, but I give you a pound, yes? And I give you back the muff, too. And, look, I give you a new paper bag for her. And one day when the war is over, if you like, I give you a job in furs. Yes? And now,' he took Vicky's hand with a sly, delicate touch, 'you give me a kiss. Yes?'

She went home with a pound, a fine paper bag and the muff. A few days later a frozen-looking beggar woman called at the house and she was able to give it away.

Mollie never enquired about it.

But then Vicky hardly saw her again for the next five or six years. War and the turmoil of her own life whirled her away from friends and relations. The next time they met was fleetingly a year later at a subdued gathering where nobody felt inclined to talk about earthly possessions.

CHAPTER ELEVEN

ONE afternoon the following year at the beginning of winter Granny sat down on a stiff chair in her Oxford Road kitchen with her knitting in her hands and she died. She was eighty-two. This stroke was the second she had had: she must have passed swiftly into unconsciousness and so out of this life without, so it was confidently assumed, any suffering or knowledge of her end. It was a kind and merciful finish to her brave, busy life.

It had been a chilly summer of defeats and disappointments. Rommel had driven the Eighth Army back across the desert into Egypt. The greatest Russian cities had been virtually destroyed; 9,000 bombs fell on Sebastopol in eight days in addition to the fiercest shelling ever known in warfare. German U-boats were sinking an average of twenty-four merchant ships a week in the Atlantic: and Churchill was daring to forecast that the worst days of the struggle were still to come and that 1943 was going to be a terrible year for the Allies.

Winter had set in early. Since August mists had been sliding up from the river at sundown and cold squalls of rain stripped the trees of their leaves and beat them down into a squelchy, slippery surface on the pavements. Sharp winds whipped up the dust at street corners. People wrapped their old, patched clothes about them and spoke apprehensively of the months to come. Winter was no longer the friendly season of parties, of cosy beds and crackling frost, of Sunday afternoon tea by the fire, with hot buttered toast and the muffin man ringing his bell outside in the street, of long, lovely evenings by lamplight with books and music and friends and drawing-boards and embroidery and the fragrance of brandy in warmed glasses, of skating on the Serpentine and skiing in the Alps and ocean cruises in search of the sun. Winter was an enemy, was a fearful journey through darkness and doubt, was a drabness and desolation, was mean as a miser with its tiny portions of margarine and dried egg, its meagre fires burning meekly in grates where the flames had once been as brilliant and lithe as flamenco dancers. The way through the cold and the dark seemed interminable; every step was painful.

It was a subdued party that assembled for the funeral in the Oxford Road drawing-room that murky December morning. The coffin, made of some pale wood, looked rather pretty strewn with boughs of evergreen and a few small wreaths of anemones and hellebore and white chrysanthemums and some out-of-season violets and snowdrops that someone had managed to procure. This might be the bleakest moment in a bitter war but Granny was not going to be allowed to go to her long rest without some of the flowers she had enjoyed so much. Although everyone looked pale, no one wore black, no one was weeping. She had not been that sort of person; it was not that sort of death.

Nevertheless, in that friendly room, still delicately

scented by the spikes of lavender that Granny had plucked from her bushes in the summer, putting them in a narrow vase on the mantelpiece to dry ready for the Christmas crop of lavender bags, there was a sense of finality that was almost historic. It was as though an epoch had, with quiet dignity, come to an end. At least that was how it seemed to the grandchildren. Women like Granny were so rare now — strong-minded, impulsive women who wore their skirts and their hair long, women whose attitude to emotions and to bodily functions was so natural that it was almost innocent, who were unafraid of Freud's bogymen and whose naturalness, like that of healthy wild animals, contained its own laws, its own modesty and sensible taboos. Such women, a species that seemed doomed to gradual extinction, had a marvellous way with babies, were content to devote themselves whole-heartedly to their family without serious thought of a profession, without a sense of inferiority at not having a classy, part-time job; women who believed in keeping up appearances, however stark the underlying reality might be, who lived in sober fear of the seven deadly sins, who brought up their children to respect, even though they could not understand, that original Artist who had created the universe, even though their own notion of the Almighty might have grown hazy beneath the impact of scientific discoveries and the massive waves of humanist materialism — steady, unspectacular women who believed that hard, honest work brought salvation and heart's ease. The grandchildren began to understand Granny's instinctive and intense dislike of *commonness*, they could see why she had always encouraged them to be resourceful, had praised their own small, creative efforts and esteemed so highly the touch of originality.

Her large, black umbrella leaned against the wall by the door; an old pair of slippers still lay by the coal scuttle; no one had thought to take away her floppy garden hat that rested upside down on the piano containing in it a handful of brown rose petals and a few withered jasmine flowers — the beginning of a pot-pourri mixture that she had felt too tired to go on with. From one of the shelves along the wall her portrait bust — 'A Young Mother' — looked down on them all — a strong, modest, sweet face with rather untidy hair arranged in a knot at her neck and a fichu that looked as though she had carelessly flung it round her shoulders catching it at her throat with a brooch — an old-fashioned face, but yet ageless.

'I do hope,' whispered Jocelyn to his mother, 'that this house won't pass out of the family. It's such a nice, kind place.' He was a thoughtful, rather powerful-looking boy with something about him that suggested John when young, a certain watchfulness and alertness, as though he were always one step ahead of the general conversation, already thinking what people were going to say next.

'Hush, dear, hush. Perhaps your Uncle John will —' Joyce hesitated; even she, with all her natural generosity of mind, could not imagine that John would *give* it to anyone. 'Perhaps he'll let you or Bruce buy it one day, when you're thinking of setting up house on your own.'

'A remarkable woman, your grandmother,' murmured Cousin Cedric, sitting by Betty's side. He had made a long, cold journey up from the country and was wrapped up in layers of wool, muffled to the tip of his nose in scarves. 'A great strength in that family. You must remind me to tell you —'

'Well then, are we all here?' said John. 'Where's Angus, Joyce?'

'He's taking Bruce straight to the church.'

'Oh yes, I remember. Bruce is going to play the organ, isn't he?.'

'The change that came over your grandmother when your grandfather died,' went on Cousin Cedric. 'The way she pulled herself together. They said she'd always been such a madcap!'

'Sink or swim, I suppose,' said Betty, who didn't feel like talking just then.

'The cars should be along any minute now,' said Salisbury, looking at his watch.

'I'd hoped there might be funeral horses,' whispered Deborah to Billy, whom she had married that summer. 'You know, with plumes and long black manes and tails'

'Hush,' said Billy. 'I don't think we ought to talk.'

Lucky Billy, who was being deftly side-stepped by the war, for whom life nearly always went well — he was thinking of the buildings he would design when the bombs stopped falling and people all came home again, lofty great buildings with immense windows and perhaps with secluded courtyards where fountains could leap and sparkle.

'The undertaker said eleven-thirty,' said Clara.

'Excuse me a minute,' Sarah stood up and went groggily out of the room. She was expecting her first child soon and was feeling ill. Her face was pale and rather haggard; she looked much older, as though life was battering her. She was having to admit to herself, inch by sticky inch, that this marriage on which she had embarked with such cheerful hope was no great shakes. Her husband was, basically, rather cold. Or was it timidity? Whatever it was, he did not have enough force or fire to obliterate the memory of that other one — and the more he tried to love her the more did she become conscious of all she was missing.

'Poor old you,' whispered Betty when her cousin crept back and sat down by her side. 'Do you feel horribly sick?'

'I do rather. It's so humiliating when one's body refuses to behave itself.'

'I'll look up one of Granny's recipes when I get home and send it to you.'

It was sad, Betty thought, that Granny couldn't just have managed to last out to welcome Sarah's child. She had always been so proud of Sarah, of her looks, her talents (she had more innate artistic skill than any of the other grandchildren, more verve and inspiration) and her social successes. In a crisis like this she would have known exactly what to do for the beastly morning sickness — raspberry leaves, or lime flowers, or some other gentle herbal concoction would have soothed it away. It would have distressed her to see Sarah like this with her green face and shadows under her lovely eyes.

The telephone rang, bright as ever.

'I'll go,' volunteered Clara.

Dorothy looked across at Bernard. Could this be Ralph? She had written to tell him of Granny's death but hardly expected that he would be allowed away from school for the funeral. But he might have managed it — he was so unpredictable and loyal, no one quite like him, she thought.

Clara returned looking perplexed. 'It was a man,' she said. 'He didn't tell me who he was. It was an elderly voice and he said, "You won't know me, but I had the honour of meeting your mother. She was a very lovely woman. I only met her once but I never forgot her. I am sorry she has gone." And then he rang off.'

Maud blushed with pleasure. 'What a lovely thing to have said about her! What a nice message!'

226

'Here are the cars,' said Bernard quietly from his post by the window. 'They've come.'

He went to open the door. The others buttoned up their coats and pulled on their gloves and looked to see they had a large hankie, just in case they broke down. Then, one by one, they followed the coffin and left the house in Oxford Road. John, the last to go, looked up at the grubby, menacing sky and went back for Granny's umbrella before closing the front door behind him.

It was bitterly cold and desolate in the Perivale churchyard where Granny was buried by the side of her young husband. The service had been bearable, even though the heating in the church was almost non-existent. The minister's utterances had been moving; Bruce had played the organ splendidly — Granny would have been thrilled to hear him. Out of doors, however, standing round the grave, a dreary melancholy invaded most of them. The air was the colour of ashes; a few dry, dirty snowflakes blew around their bowed heads. An icy air stream was flowing right across the plains of Northern Europe, robbing life of all zest. Sarah felt vilely ill. Deborah reached for Billy's hand and clung on to it. Mollie, shivering inside her expensive Persian lamb coat, remembered the brandy at home in the pantry and wished she had thought of bringing a little flask with her so that she could manage a surreptitious nip. Vicky thought of Diana, to whose funeral she had not, of course, gone and she had to fight back a flood of emotional tears. Poor Diana, oh, poor little Diana. How beastly she had been not to comfort her that summer night when Diana had cried out that she had such a pain in her heart. Was this, she wondered, the sum of living — this clayey soil, this drizzle of snow, these people standing round with pale cheeks and red noses? Betty thought, we shall not all sleep, but we shall all be changed, in a moment, in the twinkling of an eye, at the last trump: for the trumpet shall sound, and the dead shall be raised incorruptible — for this corruptible must put on incorruption — oh heavens, what does it all mean, what does it — and she longed to get home and hug her warm, chubby son and write a long letter to James overseas in a hot climate. Dorothy, spartan in her Harris tweed coat among her fur-clad in-laws, concentrated on her surroundings, looking for bright details. She always said that religion enmeshed people who might otherwise struggle to get out of their miserable living conditions, that it was a tangle of words and subterfuges and that she, for one, did not believe in a resurrection or any sort of life after death. She noticed a sparrow creeping into the shelter of a rose-bush, remarked to herself that the ivy climbing up the side of the tombstone of an adjoining grave had handsome, glossy leaves and would look very well worked into the present embroidery she took up every evening when the blackout curtains were drawn. The winter affected Dorothy less than the others. She enjoyed a struggle, be it with a political opponent, the defects of her own character, or the inclement elements. She stood very still, with her back straight and stiff, trying to memorize the shape and colour of the ivy.

After it was all over they stood about clasping their hands and looking past each other into the soot-coloured distance. They wanted to go their separate ways and get on with the business of living but could not yet quite bring themselves to say good-bye. They were all feeling dejected and oddly vulnerable and wanted the mute comfort of family ties for a little longer.

'Now then,' said John who had foreseen what the prevailing mood would be. 'Come along all of you. I've laid on a luncheon party at a hotel in Hammersmith Broadway. Mother wouldn't want us to mope. A spot of food'll do us all good.'

'I'm not weally dwessed for a party,' said Maud.

'How thoughtful of you, John!' said Dorothy.

'Do you think you can manage?' Betty asked Sarah.

'I think Uncle John's right and a spot of food'll do me good.'

'That's the spirit!'

'How very generous of John!' exclaimed Joyce.

'And how unlike him,' added Clara dryly. 'It's hard to believe."

'People do change, you know,' said Joyce.

It was discovered later that John had not changed, that this lavish lunch was not provided from some new source of bounty in him. From small economies here and there and acts of self-denial Granny had managed to scrape together a few savings. It was really only a nominal amount but it did represent care and self-respect. It was enough to see her decently buried, not that any of the family would have grudged paying for this themselves, but they assumed that John would have arranged all that. Out of the money she left behind John also arranged that Granny should pay for the lunch.

This was the last party Granny gave. Had the family known the truth they would probably have considered it too macabre, too unsuitable, and would have gone home to their one rasher of bacon and egg and their ounce of butter and cheese. Being ignorant of the facts, however, they felt free to enjoy themselves as Granny would have wished.

It was a good party.

In the days before the fly-over Hammersmith Broadway was almost unequalled in London for ugliness. It was dingy, mingy, without balance, a hotchpotch of converging roads, a dreary meeting-place of mediocrities, a broadway that was permanently constipated by too much traffic, sallow, sluggish. But inside the hotel that stood near the Broadway with incongruous gaiety, upstairs in the private dining-room Johnnie had reserved for them this family of artists did not worry about Hammersmith's ugliness. They had had enough of mourning and regret for that day. They were numb and they were hungry and with their knives, forks, spoons and clinking glasses they set to with a will and presently felt able to face the world again.

For a war-time meal the fare was first-rate and John had also ordered red wine to give them all new courage. Even Dorothy consented to partake of a glass, holding it daintily by the stem as though she were not sure of the proper way to approach the drink, sipping from the very edge, her lips only just touching the rim. Yes, it was right and proper to round off the funeral like this. Granny, such a devotee of parties and eating, would have approved whole-heartedly. She had always been one for casting off grief as vigorously as possible. They could almost hear her telling them to have another helping of sprouts and just make room for one more potato and yes, I don't think another glass of wine will hurt you, just this once, it'll put a little colour back into your cheeks, love. Fancy John seeing to all this for them. How good of him! How they had all misjudged him!

Dorothy, who found herself seated by his side, said kindly, 'And how are you feeling, John? In yourself, I mean? Are you feeling stronger again?'

'Judge for yourself, Dorothy, judge for yourself,' he

230

stretched across the table to take another slice of bread. 'It isn't really in my nature to cut down on anything. But I have to learn to obey, don't I? Ugh, this bread — pappy stuff!'

'You must let me give you some of the bread I make. It's very wholesome. Bernard says he's never been so healthy as on this war-time diet.'

'You always did encourage him to be a bit of an ascetic, didn't you?' John gave her a mischievous side-long glance. 'What news of Trotsky now? I suppose you know he's a marked man? They're hunting him down.'

'We are all marked men,' countered Dorothy with quiet dignity. 'We are all being hunted down.' She turned to Betty, on her left. 'How are you, dear? Do you get letters through from James all right?' She liked this niece, finding her sensible and sympathetic. Of all the many letters she had received when Diana had left her, Betty's had been one of the kindest.

'Yes, he writes quite often.'

'How is he managing? Does he find it bearable?'

'I think so. He seems to quite like India.'

'That's a magnificent jersey you're wearing.' Salisbury called across the table to Deborah. 'All those colours — you look like a garden in June.'

'Such intricate stitches,' said Joyce, looking closer. 'Where did you manage to get it, dear?'

'As a matter of fact,' replied Deborah, 'Billy knitted it for me.'

'Billy?'

A new warmth diffused itself through the gathering, This was the real thing. They regarded Billy tenderly and chuckled.

'Yes, it was a complete surprise. I didn't know anything about it. He used to hide himself away in the lavatory and knit there. I used to wonder why he spent so long there, if he was ill, or anything.'

Everyone laughed delightedly. Billy grinned, in a manner that made him look rather wolfish, and twisted his long fingers together under the table.

'Do you think there'll be a socialist government after the war?' he asked Dorothy, to change the conversation.

'I wouldn't like to say,' came the discreet reply.

'Just as well for you you wouldn't, Dorothy,' laughed John.

'We had some good arguments in the old days, didn't we, John?' said Dorothy. 'We used to flame at each other. Do you know,' she admitted, 'I always rather enjoyed a good argument.'

'Salisbury—' Clara laid a restraining hand on her husband's arm. 'Need you smoke? I mean, is it really necessary between courses? You know what the doctor said.'

Salisbury was not at all well: the illness that was to lay him low had already gripped him. He sometimes looked prematurely aged. But today he was casting it aside. He was so glad to be with all the family again, so pleased to have both his daughters near him. They were both far off in the country now and he missed them more than he could tell them. Even when they did manage to journey up to London they did not necessarily come to see him. Once, when he knew Betty was coming to town he scoured the shops, queued up in the wind, managed to buy several delicacies including a beautiful piece of turbot that he proposed to cook in a style fit for a banquet. But Betty had said, 'Oh, Pa, I'm terribly sorry, but I've accepted an invitation to go out to dinner.' And she had changed her dress and telephoned for a taxi and gone out and left him.

'How do you think Sarah looks?' Reggie gently enquired of Vicky.

Vicky blinked and looked down the table to where Sarah sat at the other end. It hadn't occurred to her that Sarah ever looked anything but marvellous. Just as Maud had been the acknowledged beauty of her parents' generation so Sarah was the queen of hers. Elegant, glamorous, stylish, amusing — Sarah was distinct from the rest of them. She nervously fingered the brass buttons on her khaki jacket and said she thought Sarah looked fine.

'Do you really? I'm not very happy about her.' As the Staffordshire intonation had always come out in Granny's speech when she was excited or deeply moved, so did Reggie's voice take on his native Yorkshire at certain moments. 'I think she's pining for something. I think she's lonely.' His voice burred; he might have been on the moors of the West Riding. 'You know, Sarah needs people. She's really splendid with people. I feel her life's taken a wrong twist somewhere.'

Vicky raised her eyes to her uncle's handsome face. She felt flattered that he should be talking to her so intimately; this had never happened before.

'Do you remember when Deborah and Billy got married?' Sarah's laughing voice gave the lie to these speculations. 'They both looked so young, a couple of children, that the hotel where they were going for their honeymoon thought they were up to no good. It took quite some time to persuade them to let you have the room, didn't it, Debbie?'

'You see,' said Reggie softly. 'With the family she's all right. Her gay self.'

'*Waiter!*' shouted John. 'What are you dawdling for? I want my *pudding*.'

'Coming, sir, coming.'

'What is it? What did I order?' John scanned the menu. 'Apple charlotte or trifle. Ye gods, is that really the best you can do for us.' When he was cross his face seemed to puff out: he now looked like a petulant, over-fed baby.

'Well, sir, yes, sir. Rations, you know.'

'I'm very partial to apple charlotte,' declared Dorothy.

'We've got a good selection of cheeses,' said the waiter. 'And you would like coffee, wouldn't you? Here? Or downstairs?'

'We'll stay here,' said John. 'In our own warmth.'

'Uncle John,' came Jocelyn's clear young voice in the silence that preceded the pudding. 'What's going to happen about Granny's house? You're not going to let strangers live in it?'

He had been worrying about this, on and off, throughout the funeral service, seeing in his mind's eye the figure of Granny as she bustled round her kitchen stove pulling out from the oven cakes that smelt of vanilla, hearing, like an echo, the shouts of children swinging high at the bottom of the garden, the sound of singing round the piano in the evening.

'Ah-ha —' said John slyly, having already more or less decided that he would be able to sell it for a good sum.

'I expect he'll give it to you all, darlin',' piped up Mollie.

'Bruce —' Jocelyn, a canny boy, was not entirely satisfied and appealed to his elder brother.

'I've managed a little cream,' announced the waiter, bearing in the pudding.

'Top of the milk, don't you mean?' said Betty.

'I've just discovered we have a very strong connexion with the Wedgwood family,' Cousin Cedric spoke up firmly, steering the talk to higher levels. 'Very strong indeed.'

'The Wedgwoods,' said John, 'are all very well in their way. But for real skill and art, for the best pottery figures, they can't anywhere hold a candle to our lot. Ask any collector or connoisseur.'

'Yes, there was great-great-great-uncle Ralph, for instance —'

'And Enoch —'

'And wasn't there an Aaron —?'

'Yes — and a Moses —'

'All master potters.'

'All artists in their way.'

Family pride rumbled importantly. Cousin Cedric brought out the family tree and pointed. Dorothy felt bored and irritated. Really, they did make such a fuss, this lot, about their past and their potters. Potters! It wasn't anything to be so very excited about. She thought of her own mother and her own particular pride possessed her. *Her* mother — dignified, uncomplaining, who had really had much more to put up with than Granny — she *was* someone — She looked around for Vicky, wanting to talk to her and make jokes.

'No —' John pushed back his plate of trifle. 'I can't eat this stuff. Not even for the sake of beating the Boche.'

'I think I want to stand up,' said Salisbury, and did so. Some of the others followed his example.

'Bwing in the cheese,' ordered Maud. 'And coffee to follow.'

Mollie went round to John, bent down and whispered in his ear.

'No, old girl,' he replied. 'I'm not handing round brandy and liqueurs with the coffee. Have another glass of wine. There's still some left in the bottle.'

'You're looking very smart in your uniform, sweetheart.' Mollie turned to Vicky. 'So you're driving lorries now? What happened to the nursing?'

'I got rather ill. I was sent to work in a sanatorium. To nurse people with t.b. We were terribly short-staffed and overworked. We had literally to run nearly all day, from patient to patient. Some of them were very bad and had to have oxygen. We had to move the great cylinders about. They were ever so heavy. And I hated having to give people injections — you know, having to stick needles into them. Anyway, I got ill with pneumonia and had to be in bed in the hospital for about two months. Silly, wasn't it? They were afraid I might have caught t.b. A lot of the staff did pick it up. But I was lucky and didn't.'

'Do you like the driving?'

'Yes, I do. And I love working out of doors. And I like the soldiers I work with and the other A.T.S.'

'And do you think we'll win the war, Bernard?' asked Salisbury.

'God knows. But I'm afraid it's going on for a long, long time.'

'You were always a pessimist, old chap!'

Bernard pushed up his face into a wry little smile that made him look rather like a goblin.

'My dear Salisbury, the pessimist's the only thinker who's always been right. He's the only prophet who's never been a failure. Extreme cheerfulness is a sign of lunacy! I ask you, Salisbury — when have human affairs ever shown the slightest sign of improving?'

'Oh, Bernard, for heaven's sake! Life's not as bad as that!'

'Life's very difficult, Salisbury. And it's going to get more difficult. There's nothing you or I or anyone can do about it.'

He grinned again and turned away. It was never easy with him to tell when he was pulling your leg and when he was being serious. In his work he was always romantic, always striving for a deeper, finer relationship between truth and beauty, between the real and the ideal, what was and what might be. He was probably much more of an optimist than he cared to admit.

'So Ralph couldn't manage to come?' Reggie joined Dorothy, who was standing by the window looking down into the dust-coloured Broadway where the early dusk was already starting to soften some of the crude outlines. In the corner of the room where the window joined the wall, John had put Granny's time-honoured umbrella: Reggie ran his hand up the spokes, touched the smooth, curved handle.

'No, Reggie. I didn't think he would. The journey wasn't really necessary.'

'How is he?'

'Restless. What else can you expect?'

'I suppose he'll be going on to a university soon.'

'Oh no, Reggie, I'm afraid not. He's counting the weeks to his next birthday. On the stroke of seventeen he's going to volunteer for the Fleet Air Arm. He says he can't begin to think about his own life until we've given Hitler what he deserves.'

'I thought you weren't supposed to know about that, Dorothy?'

'Not know? Oh, Reggie!' She turned away from the window, looking straight at him. 'It doesn't need words to tell me what's going on in my son's mind and heart.'

'No, I suppose not. Maud's the same where Sarah's concerned. I'm afraid she's rather worried about her. We think she's unhappy. We don't think this marriage of hers is going to last.'

'No? Oh, Reggie, I am sorry.'

'You have very fearless eyes, Dorothy, if you don't mind me saying so.'

237

'Have I? They've always served me well. They're strong and steady. I can see a long way. I never have headaches.'

As she grew older Dorothy's eyes had changed colour from the fresh blue of her youth to a clear grey. They were, as Reggie had said, brave eyes. Confronting her unwavering, quiet regard, people always found it completely impossible to lie to her. They hoodwinked her sometimes, making themselves out to be better than they were; they glossed over facts they thought best disguised; but they could never bring themselves actually to speak an untruth to her.

'I have never cared for the sea, Reggie,' she said. 'All that tossing about! All that foaming and churning!' She lightly ran her fingertips over her forehead. 'And Ralph gets sick so easily. I don't know how he'll stand it. Really I don't.'

Reggie put a gentle hand on her shoulder and they stood thus for a few moments, their backs to the assembly, sharing the knowledge that in the last resort there was nothing you could do to protect those you loved from harm.

'I feel we ought to be *doing* something, Betty,' said Sarah, helping herself to another cup of black coffee. 'Playing games, or acting, or something.'

'Perhaps they've got a radio in the hotel. Perhaps we could dance.'

'With me in my state! Me and Uncle John waltzing tummy to tummy! Met any gorgeous new men lately, Betty?'

'As a matter of fact —' Betty sat down again by her side and started to talk to her very softly.'

'Seeing Granny's umbrella over there makes me feel she's going to come bustling in at any moment and offer us fudge out of an oven tray,' said Deborah.

'What was the story you started to tell me once about Granny and the turkey?' asked Billy. 'It had something to do with her umbrella.'

'Oh, that!' Deborah laughed. 'Well, Granny was rushing round on Christmas Eve one year, doing all the shopping. She was late with it and in a great hurry. She'd got a heavy basket on one arm and that old umbrella on the other. She hadn't bothered to roll it up, or anything. It just flopped about. She felt it was a bit heavy, but she was in too much of a rush to stop and look. And when she got home she found she'd somehow hooked up a turkey with it and it'd fallen down inside. She was in an awful state about it and dashed back to the butcher to own up.'

'And what happened then?'

'Uncle Bernard,' implored Sarah. 'Daddy always says you're the life and soul of parties. Couldn't you get something going. Even the Hokey Cokey would be better than nothing.'

'My dancing days are over, for the duration.'

'Nonsense. Everyone's always said you were such a marvellous dancer.'

'Did they? Well, as a matter of fact I have thought — Vicky, Vicky, here a moment,' he called to his daughter. 'I've been meaning to ask you, Vicky. Next time you come on leave will you take me to the Hammersmith Palais and give me some lessons? Bring me up to date with some of the new steps?'

'I'd love to. There's a soldier in our regiment, an ex-Streatham Locarno gigolo, who's taught me how to tango really properly. We go to dances together, in drill halls. And we do passionate tangos. It's a scream!' Vicky had been drinking too much wine and it was making her silly.

Dorothy beckoned her rather sternly to come over

239

by the window. Reggie moved across to talk to Bernard. Bruce and Jocelyn were playing chess with a little pocket set. Angus talked to Salisbury about the mighty cricketing days of the past.

'How's the Royal College of Art, Reggie? Any promising students?'

'I'm hoping the war'll break down some of our national prejudices,' replied Reggie. 'Get rid of our foolish insularity. It's about time we allowed ourselves to be influenced by some of the modern Continental experiments in form and design.'

'Modern,' reflected Bernard. 'Modern — everything's got to be modern. What is *modern*? A new trend, something modish, something springing off at a tangent, a development? You know, Reggie, the whole development of art today is wrapped up with the inner meaning of the war. The conflict of opinion in art reflects the bitter struggle now taking place.'

'Spengler again!' smiled Reggie.

'Actually, I was thinking of Toynbee. Listen —' Out came one of Bernard's famous sketch-books and he started to read: '— if we are to attempt to ascertain the limits of any civilization we find that the aesthetic test is the surest as well as the subtlest and that the chiselling of a stone is as capable of bearing testimony to the existence of the culture that fashioned it, with as clear a voice, as the masterpiece of a great poet or the life of a great saint or the career of a great statesman —'

'Yes, perhaps —' Reggie preferred teaching to expounding controversial theories.

Bernard slipped the sketch-book back into his pocket. 'This conflict in the world of art first became apparent at the beginning of the present century,' he said. 'The post-Impressionists — that was the first sign — at least, one of the first —'

'Yes, perhaps — can I have a look at your sketch-book? May I?'

'Certainly,'

Reggie turned the pages, glancing at the quick, sure sketches, the sudden lines of inspiration, the notes, the quotations.

'You must have got dozens of these, Bernard. I can't remember a time when you weren't pulling one out of your pocket. Do you keep them all?'

'I'm one of those tiresome people who can never throw anything away. Dorothy gets quite vexed with me!'

'They'll be worth a fortune one of these days. You should see what people'll pay for a tiny sketch by Delacroix, for instance.'

'You always were a flatterer, Reggie! I have no illusions about my merits as an artist. I've never been an influence. I don't stand out. I'm not nearly as good as my father would have been had he lived. Probably I'm not much more than a good craftsman. But at least I've always tried to do my best. I've never cheated or turned away just because something was difficult.'

'After this beastly war, Bernard, I think you'll come into your own. I think the tides of fortune will carry you high.

Bernard gave a sardonic smile. 'One never knows. But one thing I do know, Reggie, that it's the most difficult thing in the world, in fact almost impossible, to move up out of one social class into a higher.'

Reggie felt that a lot of experience lay behind that remark and that there must be unplumbed, secret depths in Bernard's nature. He went on turning the pages of the sketch-book. 'What's this?' he asked.

Bernard looked over his shoulder and read out, with a faulty Italian accent:

'Com' esser, donna, può quel ch'alcun vede
Per lunga sperienza, che più dura
L'immagin viva in pietra alpestra e dura,
Che 'l suo fattor, che gli anni in cener riede?'—

'That's by the great old man with the broken nose. Michelangelo — who else?'

'Daddy, I think I ought to be getting back.' Sarah came across and joined them.

'We'll take you home, darling.'

'Talking of dancing, Sarah,' put in Bernard impishly, 'I was reading Dunne's *An Experiment With Time* the other day and in the night I dreamed I was dancing with a midget. It was very odd!'

Sarah laughed, showing her small, perfect teeth. 'Uncle Bernard, you're terrific!'

'Yes,' said Dorothy, 'we'd better be getting along. I've got a batch of bread I must make. And we want to be home by dark.'

'I think I'll just take a turn along by the river,' said Bernard. 'There's a beautiful curve along past Hammersmith Mall. I'll catch you up. You go on in front.'

'Very well, darling,' agreed Dorothy, who had at last accepted the truth that people did not change but only became more so.

They all looked around for their coats, patted their hair into place under their hats, muffled themselves up in scarves and lingered over their good-byes because none of them fancied going out into that cold murkiness where the darkness was creeping up like an enemy.

'You must let us pay our share,' said Dorothy quietly to John. 'We would like it all to be fair.'

'Shouldn't dream of it, Dorothy. Glad you've enjoyed it. Granny would have been pleased.' He turned up his fur collar, pushed past her out of the room and shouted at someone down in the hotel lobby to go and tell his chauffeur he was ready.

'You didn't ever tell me the end of that story about Granny and the turkey,' said Billy, taking Deborah's hand as they went out into the street, thankful he had got her alone to himself once more. 'What happened?'

'Let me see, where was I? Yes — well she went back to the butcher to own up and she found he was shut. She was in an awful state not knowing what to do. So she knocked on their side door, banged and banged with her umbrella till somebody came.'

'And then?'

'Apparently they didn't believe her story. She probably looked a bit wild and eccentric — her hair was probably very untidy — and they thought she was a bit touched and making it up. They told her to go home. So she did, and that year they had an extra turkey!'

'She was rather marvellous, wasn't she?' Vicky said to her mother as they walked towards the bus stop.

'Who, darling?'

'Granny, of course.'

'Oh yes — Granny. People have always said she was.'

'I mean — managing like she did. 'A widow with five children —'

'It was the same with your other grandmother, you know. With my mother. She managed much better than Granny. She was a much finer person.'

'Yes, but your mother did have some money, didn't she? I mean, it must have been a bit easier for her.'

'Granny was surrounded by friends who helped her. My mother had to move right away and make another home for her children. Somewhere where no one knew about things. Because of the disgrace.'

'Disgrace? What disgrace?'

Dorothy didn't reply and Vicky, glancing shyly sideways, saw that her face wore that mysterious Mona Lisa smile that betokened some painful secret.

'I'll tell you some time,' said Dorothy presently. 'Perhaps.'

It seemed to Vicky that a new door suddenly swung open and she looked down a strange road towards an unexplored country. Apprehension possessed he; but it was an apprehension that contained a germ of satisfaction because she sensed that at last she was going to begin to understand obscure fears and presentiments that had haunted her since childhood, words half heard, quick flashes of understanding between adults, deception pulled down over their face like a visor — Yes, one day she must venture out down that road to explore that dark, unknown country. But not yet, not yet.

'Hullo!' the familiar, melodious voice caught up with them. 'Let's hope we don't have long to wait for a bus!'

'I thought you were going for a walk by the river, Bernard.'

'Too cold, my dear. And besides, you never know, Ralph may have turned up after all.'

'What was that poem you were reading to Uncle Reggie?'

'Ah — Michelangelo —

> *Sì che mill' anni dopo la partita*
> *Quanto e voi bella fusti, e quant' io lasso*
> *Sì veggia, e com' amarvi io non fui stolto.*

Michelangelo — what a life he had!'

'What does it mean exactly?'

'Shakespeare said more or less the same thing — in his Eighteenth Sonnet.'

'Remarkable woman!' said Cousin Cedric, standing on the curb, looking for a taxi to wave to. 'I remember being brought to visit you all in Beaufort Street, when I was a little boy and Granny not long a widow, and there you all were, making music like a company of strolling players, fiddling and celloing and making great crescendos on the piano.'

'I shall always remember Granny and that beetroot!' laughed Sarah, who was feeling much better again. 'The way she sat there in the kitchen saying she must have some beetroot to go with the ham! And then went straight out to the greengrocer in the middle of tea!'

'Yes, she was always practical,' said Cousin Cedric. 'Always knew what to *do*.'

'And do you remember that party when we all danced wild Cossack dances?' said Betty.

'I really can't get over John giving us that lunch!' said Joyce.

'I know,' agreed Clara thoughtfully.

'And wasn't it lovely,' said Maud, 'that old gentleman winging up. Like a happy ending. And Johnnie turning up twumps! It was a beautiful funewal!'

'Yes, it was a surprise about John,' Clara once more admitted. There was a small frown on her forehead and a touch of reserve in her voice. She couldn't help feeling there was something a bit odd about it.

'Damn!' exclaimed John as the Daimler glided across Barnes Common.

'What's the matter, your Lordship?' asked Mollie.

'The umbrella! I've left the umbrella behind. Upstairs where we had lunch. We'll have to go back.'

'Can't it wait till another day?'

'No, it certainly can *not*! I wouldn't want to leave it

about where just any common person can pick it up.'
He leaned forward to give instructions to the chauffeur.

'It looks as though it's starting to snow,' said Mollie,
realizing that although Granny might now be lying
dead in the ground her memory would go on living
with them for ever.

The chauffeur drove back to the shabby hotel and
John climbed the stairs again as quickly as he could
and rather breathlessly, because he was not at all well.
The old black umbrella was still there in the corner,
where he had left it, and he clutched at it, clasping it to
him for a moment as though it were something very
precious that he had found again after thinking he had
lost it for ever.

Mollie had got out of the car and was waiting for
him on the pavement. Snow was white on her astrakhan
hat and on the toes of her little black, high-heeled boots.
The flakes were melting into the sweep of the river by
Hammersmith Mall, were covering the flowers on the
new grave, were piling up against the dark windows of
the house in Oxford Road.

'This hateful weather,' said Mollie. 'It's so icy and
raw. Let's hope spring'll be early this year.'

John shook the umbrella and put it up, holding it
over them both to protect them from the hostile skies.
A hairpin dropped out and bounced off his hat; a small
shower of dry, sweet-scented lavender flowers and the
dust from withered leaves of mint fell on to his shoulders and for a second or two the air round them smelt
like a warm summer day.

Spring was not early but it did come eventually and
John's peculiar little meanness about the funeral party
was discovered and the usual indignant comments were
made. In due course the house in Putney passed into

246

the hands of strangers and Granny's few possessions were shared out among the family.

Her image stayed bright and true in everyone's mind; she was not the sort of person to slip easily from the memory. She seemed often to be there, somewhere in the background — an almost palpable presence in her long dress and large hat, always carrying a bag with some handwork poking out of the top, peering a little because her eyes were not very good and she had always overworked them. After the war, when Bernard's statues rose up out of bombed London, statues of recognizable human beings with balanced, fine bodies, she was there, at each unveiling, joining in the talk. When more and more great-grandchildren were born — when Sarah at last managed to put her life to rights again and moved into a large, important world of diplomacy and politics — when Vicky, exploring that strange country of which Dorothy had allowed her a glimpse, was swept out of her depth in a great storm of love and death — when Deborah and her Billy built good schools where children could sit in classrooms with sunlight pouring over them — Granny was around, applauding, encouraging, trying to help.

Bernard's lovely bronze girl, his 'Awakening', finally left his studio and went out into the world to stand in a little garden specially made for her by the Thames, near the end of Beaufort Street where they had spent their crowded childhood — the girl who was real, right down to her skeleton, who had rather ugly feet. Among the geometric modern buildings and the lugubrious and comic creatures of concrete and steel she seems almost a being from another world. A reminder of the classical world? A promise of some perfection still to come? A moment of grace? In winter-time you may think she looks rather lonely and vulnerable; but in the spring, when the leaves shield her a little and the flowers blossom in the garden and people sit there resting, she comes into her own and reminds those who look at her that human beings are just as likely to be gentle and hopeful as they are to be violent and depraved.

And should you ever happen to be in the East End of London, make your way to Bethnal Green and find its curious museum and ask the attendant there to show you Salisbury's ingenious circus. If there are not too many children milling around you may be lucky in persuading him to produce the handle and then you can make it go round and watch the little figures performing like the grandchildren did at that Christmas party so many years ago.